math
expressions

Dr. Karen C. Fuson

Watch the lemur come alive in its forest as you discover and solve math challenges.

Download the *Math Worlds AR* app available on Android or iOS devices.

Grade **4**

Volume 1

This material is based upon work supported by the
National Science Foundation
under Grant Numbers
ESI-9816320, REC-9806020, and RED-935373.

Any opinions, findings, and conclusions, or recommendations expressed in this material
are those of the author and do not necessarily reflect the views of the National Science Foundation.

ISBN 978-1-328-74383-1

4 5 6 7 8 9 10   0029   26 25 24 23 22 21 20 19

4500758407   D E F G

BIG IDEA 1 - Place Value to One Million

BIG IDEA 2 - Addition with Greater Numbers

BIG IDEA 3 - Subtraction with Greater Numbers

BIG IDEA 4 - Fluency with Multiplication and Division Within 100

BIG IDEA 1 - Dividing Whole Numbers

BIG IDEA 2 - Division Issues and Word Problems

BIG IDEA 3 - Two-Digit Divisors

BIG IDEA 4 - Analyzing Patterns

Student Resources

Dear Family:

Your child is learning math in an innovative program called *Math Expressions*. In Unit 1, your child will use place value drawings and charts to understand that the value of each place is 10 times greater than the value of the place to its right. This understanding is essential when comparing, rounding, or adding multidigit numbers. *Math Expressions* encourages children to think about "making new groups" to help them understand place values.

We call the method below "New Groups Above Method." The numbers that represent the new groups are written above the problem.

1. Add the ones:

$5 + 7 = 12$ ones
$12 = 2$ ones $+ 10$ ones,
and 10 ones $= 1$ new ten.

$$
\begin{array}{r}
\overset{1}{} \\
5,1\,7\,5 \\
+\,3,9\,6\,7 \\
\hline
2
\end{array}
$$

2. Add the tens:

$1 + 7 + 6 = 14$ tens
$14 = 4$ tens $+ 10$ tens,
and 10 tens $= 1$ new hundred.

$$
\begin{array}{r}
\overset{1\ 1}{} \\
5,1\,7\,5 \\
+\,3,9\,6\,7 \\
\hline
4\,2
\end{array}
$$

3. Add the hundreds:

$1 + 1 + 9 = 11$ hundreds
$11 = 1$ hundred $+ 10$ hundreds,
and 10 hundreds $= 1$ new thousand.

$$
\begin{array}{r}
\overset{1\ \ 1\ 1}{} \\
5,1\,7\,5 \\
+\,3,9\,6\,7 \\
\hline
1\,4\,2
\end{array}
$$

4. Add the thousands:

$1 + 5 + 3 = 9$ thousands

$$
\begin{array}{r}
\overset{1\ \ 1\ 1}{} \\
5,1\,7\,5 \\
+\,3,9\,6\,7 \\
\hline
9,1\,4\,2
\end{array}
$$

We call the following method "New Groups Below Method." The steps are the same, but the new groups are written below the addends.

1.
$$
\begin{array}{r}
5,1\,7\,5 \\
+\,3,9\,6\,7 \\
\hline
1\,2
\end{array}
$$

2.
$$
\begin{array}{r}
5,1\,7\,5 \\
+\,3,9\,6\,7 \\
\hline
1\,1 \\
4\,2
\end{array}
$$

3.
$$
\begin{array}{r}
5,1\,7\,5 \\
+\,3,9\,6\,7 \\
\hline
1\,1\,1 \\
1\,4\,2
\end{array}
$$

4.
$$
\begin{array}{r}
5,1\,7\,5 \\
+\,3,9\,6\,7 \\
\hline
1\,1\,1 \\
9,1\,4\,2
\end{array}
$$

> It is easier to see the totals for each column (12 and 14) and adding is easier because you add the two numbers you see and then add the 1.

Activities and games to build fluency with multiplication and division are included at the end of this unit. It is important that your child maintains his or her home practice with basic multiplication and division.

Sincerely,
Your child's teacher

Estimada familia:

Su niño está aprendiendo matemáticas mediante el programa *Math Expressions*. En la Unidad 1, se usarán dibujos y tablas de valor posicional para comprender que el valor de cada lugar es 10 veces mayor que el valor del lugar a su derecha. Comprender esto es esencial para comparar, redondear o sumar números de varios dígitos. *Math Expressions* enseña a pensar en "formar grupos nuevos" para comprender los valores posicionales.

Este método se llama "Método de Grupos nuevos arriba." Los números que representan los grupos nuevos se escriben arriba del problema:

1. Suma las unidades:

5 + 7 = 12 unidades
12 = 2 unidades + 10 unidades,
y 10 unidades = 1 nueva decena.

```
    1
  5, 1 7 5
+ 3, 9 6 7
─────────
        2
```

2. Suma las decenas:

1 + 7 + 6 = 14 decenas
14 = 4 decenas + 10 decenas,
y 10 decenas = 1 nueva centena.

```
   1 1
  5, 1 7 5
+ 3, 9 6 7
─────────
      4 2
```

3. Suma las centenas:

1 + 1 + 9 = 11 centenas
11 = 1 centenas + 10 centenas,
y 10 centenas = 1 nuevo millar.

```
  1 1 1
  5, 1 7 5
+ 3, 9 6 7
─────────
    1 4 2
```

4. Suma los millares:

1 + 5 + 3 = 9 millares

```
  1  1 1
  5, 1 7 5
+ 3, 9 6 7
─────────
  9, 1 4 2
```

Este método se llama "Método de Grupos nuevos abajo". Los pasos son iguales, pero los nuevos grupos se escriben abajo de los sumandos:

1.
```
  5, 1 7 5
+ 3, 9 6 7
─────────
      1 2
```

2.
```
  5, 1 7 5
+ 3, 9 6 7
─────────
    1
    4 2
```

3.
```
  5, 1 7 5
+ 3, 9 6 7
─────────
  1 1 1
  1 4 2
```

4.
```
  5, 1 7 5
+ 3, 9 6 7
─────────
  1 1 1
  9, 1 4 2
```

> Es más fácil ver los totales de cada columna (12 y 14) y es más fácil sumar porque sumas los dos números que ves, y luego sumas 1.

Al final de esta unidad se incluyen actividades y juegos para desarrollar la fluidez con la multiplicación y división. Es importante que su niño siga practicando las multiplicaciones y divisiones básicas en casa.

Atentamente,
El maestro de su niño

addend	factor
digit	greater than ($>$)
expanded form	inverse operations

One of two or more numbers multiplied to find a product.

Example:

$$4 \times 5 = 20$$

factor   factor   product

One of two or more numbers added together to find a sum.

Example:

$$7 + 8 = 15$$

addend   addend   sum

A symbol used to compare two numbers. The greater number is given first below.

Example:
33 > 17
33 is greater than 17.

Any of the symbols 0, 1, 2, 3, 4, 5, 6, 7, 8, or 9.

Opposite or reverse operations that undo each other. Addition and subtraction are inverse operations. Multiplication and division are inverse operations.

Examples:
$4 + 6 = 10$ so, $10 - 6 = 4$ and $10 - 4 = 6$.
$3 \times 9 = 27$ so, $27 \div 9 = 3$ and $27 \div 3 = 9$.

A way of writing a number that shows the value of each of its digits.

Example:
Expanded form of 835:
$800 + 30 + 5$
8 hundreds + 3 tens + 5 ones

less than (<)

product

order

square number

place value

standard form

The answer to a multiplication problem.

Example:
$9 \times 7 = 63$

↑
product

A symbol used to compare two numbers.
The smaller number is given first below.

Example:
$54 < 78$
54 is less than 78.

The product of a whole number and itself.

Example
$3 \times 3 = 9$

↑
square number

Arrange numbers from the least number to the greatest number or from the greatest number to the least number.

Examples:
Least to greatest: 453, 526, 571, 802
Greatest to least: 3,742; 3,608; 3,295

The form of a number written using digits.

Example:
2,145

The value assigned to the place that a digit occupies in a number.

Example:
235

↑
The 2 is in the hundreds place, so its value is 200.

word form

The form of a number written using words instead of digits.

Example:
Six hundred thirty-nine

Name Sidra SAEED

Model Hundreds

You can represent numbers by making place value drawings on a dot array.

✓ Good
A+

1. What number does this drawing show? 5,037 537
Explain your thinking.

I think that my number is right because ever there were 5 10 boxes there so that means 5 thousand. then there were 3 3 10 so 30 and 7.

Model Thousands

3 thousand

Discuss this place value drawing. Write the number of each.

3,458

2. ones: 8

3. quick tens: 56

4. hundred boxes: 4

5. thousand bars: 3

6. How many hundred boxes could we draw inside each thousand bar? Explain.

5 because 10 because
$10 \times 10 = 1000$

7. What number does this drawing show?

3,458

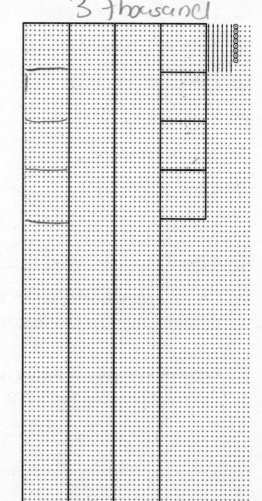

© Houghton Mifflin Harcourt Publishing Company

Model Greater Numbers

VOCABULARY
place value

Place value can also be shown without using a dot array.

8 What number does this drawing represent? Explain your thinking.

_____

_____

_____

_____

_____

What would the drawing represent if it had:

9 3 more hundred boxes? _____

10 0 hundred boxes? _____

11 2 fewer quick tens? _____

12 2 more quick tens? _____

13 0 quick tens? _____

14 5 fewer ones? _____

15 0 ones? _____

16 4 more thousand bars? _____

17 On your MathBoard, make a place value drawing for a different number that has the digits 1, 2, 7, and 9.

18 Explain how your drawing is similar to and different from the drawing for 1,279.

_____

_____

Place Value to Thousands

Practice with Place Value Drawings

Make a place value drawing for each number, using ones, quick tens, and hundred boxes.

19 6

20 3

21 603

22 300

23 63

24 32

25 325

26 285

27 109

28 573

Practice Modeling Thousands

Make a place value drawing for each number, using ones, quick tens, hundred boxes, and thousand bars.

29 2,596

30 3,045

✓ **Check Understanding**

Make a place value drawing to show 2,361. Then compare it to the place value drawing for Exercise 29 and explain the differences between the two drawings.

Place Value to Thousands

Name Sidra Saeed

The Place Value Chart

Discuss the patterns you see in the Place Value Poster below.

× 10 (Greater)

Thousands	Hundreds	Tens	ONES
1,000.	100.	10.	1.
$\frac{1,000}{1}$	$\frac{100}{1}$	$\frac{10}{1}$	$\frac{1}{1}$
$1,000.00	$100.00	$10.00	$1.00

Use your Whole Number Secret Code Cards to make numbers on the frame.

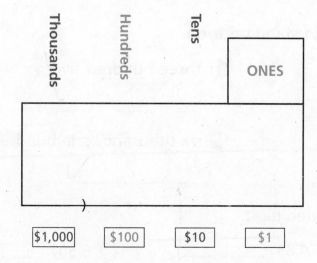

$1,000 $100 $10 $1

Write Numbers Using Expanded Form

VOCABULARY
standard form
word form
expanded form

Standard form: 8,562

Word form: eight thousand, five hundred sixty-two

Expanded form: 8,000 + 500 + 60 + 2

Read and write each number in expanded form.

1. 73 $\underline{70+3=73}$ ✓

2. 108 $\underline{100+8=108}$ ✓

3. 5,621 $\underline{5,000+600+20+1=}$ ✓
$\underline{5,621}$

4. 8,083 $\underline{8,000+80+3=8,083}$ ✓

Read and write each number in standard form.

5. 40 + 3 $\underline{43}$ ✓

6. 200 + 60 + 1 $\underline{261}$ ✓

7. 1,000 + 70 + 9 $\underline{1,079}$ ✓

8. 9,000 + 800 + 4 $\underline{9,804}$ ✓

Read and write each number in word form.

9. 400 + 40 + 1 $\underline{\text{four hunderend fourty one}}$ ✓

10. 1,000 + 50 $\underline{\text{One thousand fivtty}}$ ✓

Read and write each number in standard form.

11. thirty-five

$\underline{35}$ ✓

12. three hundred five

$\underline{305}$ ✓

13. six thousand, eight

$\underline{6,008}$ ✓

14. six thousand, one hundred eight

$\underline{6,108}$ ✓

Write the value of the underlined digit.

15. 7<u>5</u>6 $\underline{50}$ ✓

16. <u>4</u>,851 $\underline{4,000}$ ✓

17. 6,<u>5</u>07 $\underline{500}$ ✓

 Check Understanding

Explain how to use place value to write a number in standard, word, and expanded forms.

 Place Value Patterns

Summarize Rounding Rules

Use these rounding frames as a visual aid when rounding to the nearest 1,000; 100; 10.

Nearest 1,000	Nearest 100	Nearest 10
10,000	1,000	100
9,000	900	90
8,000	800	80
7,000	700	70
6,000	600	60
5,000	500	50
4,000	400	40
3,000	300	30
2,000	200	20
1,000	100	10
0	0	0

Round to the nearest thousand.

1 1,275 _____   **2** 8,655 _____   **3** 5,482 _____

4 3,804 _____   **5** 1,501 _____   **6** 9,702 _____

Round to the nearest hundred.

7 734 _____   **8** 363 _____   **9** 178 _____

10 6,249 _____   **11** 8,251 _____   **12** 8,992 _____

Round to the nearest ten.

13 87 _____   **14** 16 _____   **15** 171 _____

16 2,165 _____   **17** 5,114 _____   **18** 3,098 _____

Compare Numbers

VOCABULARY
greater than >
less than <

Discuss the problem below.

Jim has 24 trading cards and Hattie has 42 trading cards.
Who has more trading cards? How do you know?

She has more tchs.

Draw a place value model for each problem.
Write > (greater than), < (less than), or = to make
each statement true.

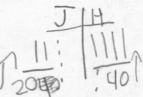

⑲ 26 ⟨<⟩ 29

⑳ 44 ⟨>⟩ 34

㉑ 26 ⟨<⟩ 62

①Go to greatest P.V
②wich digit has more blue.

Compare using >, <, or =.

㉒ 74 ⟨<⟩ 77

㉓ 85 ⟨>⟩ 58

㉔ 126 ⟨<⟩ 162

㉕ 253 ⟨>⟩ 235

㉖ 620 ◯ 602

㉗ 825 ⟨>⟩ 528

㉘ 478 ⟨<⟩ 488

㉙ 3,294 ⟨<⟩ 3,924

㉚ 8,925 ⟨<⟩ 9,825

㉛ 6,706 ⟨<⟩ 6,760

㉜ 4,106 ⟨>⟩ 4,016

㉝ 1,997 ⟨>⟩ 1,799

㉞ 9,172 ⟨<⟩ 9,712

㉟ 5,296 ⟨>⟩ 5,269

㊱ 7,684 ⟨=⟩ 7,684

Round Numbers

Order Numbers on a Number Line

VOCABULARY
order

You can **order** numbers by arranging them from the least number to the greatest number or the greatest number to the least number.

Use the number lines.

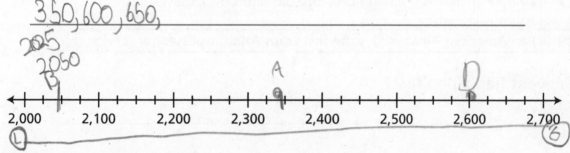

intervals

37 Draw and label a point on the number line for each number: 600, 350, 650.

38 Write the numbers in order from least to greatest.

350, 600, 650,

2025
2050

39 Draw and label a point on the number line for each number: 2,500; 2,025; 2,350; 2,575.

40 Write the numbers in order from greatest to least.

2,575, 2,500, 2,350, 2025

Write the numbers in order from least to greatest.

41 994, 748, 906, 876 748 876 906, 999

42 2,480; 2,078; 2,409 2,078, 2,409, 2,480

Write the numbers in order from greatest to least.

43 588, 836, 498, 534 498

44 2,104; 2,652; 2,008 _____

© Houghton Mifflin Harcourt Publishing Company

Order Numbers on a Timeline

The timeline is divided into 10-year periods called decades.

Events in Aviation

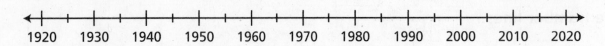

45 Draw and label a point on the timeline for each year in the table.

Year	Event
2015	The first test of a drone tracking system occurs.
1989	*Voyager 2* first encounters Neptune.
1978	The first balloon flight over the Atlantic Ocean occurs.
1927	Lindbergh makes the first non-stop solo flight over the Atlantic Ocean.
1939	Pan American Airways flies the first trans-Atlantic passenger service.

46 Which event happened first?

_____

_____

47 Write the years of the events in order from the earliest year to the latest year.

_____

48 Write a question that can be answered by the timeline. Include the answer.

_____

_____

_____

✔ **Check Understanding**

Explain a method you can use to round, compare, or order multidigit numbers.

Round Numbers

Name Sidra Khan

Discuss and Summarize

Patterns to Millions

Hundred Millions	Ten Millions	Millions	Hundred Thousands	Ten Thousands	Thousands	Hundreds	Tens	Ones
100,000,000	10,000,000	1,000,000	100,000	10,000	1,000	100	10	1
millions			*thousands*			*[ones]*		

The Patterns to Millions chart shows that each digit in the number has a place value name. When we read a number, we do not say the place value name. We say the group name.

1,000

We say the word *million* after the digits in the millions group.

We say the word *thousand* after the digits in the thousands group.

We do not say the word *ones* after the digits in the ones group.

To read greater numbers, say each group of digits as if they were in the hundreds, tens, and ones places and then add the special name for that group.

Read Numbers

Use your Whole Number Secret Code cards to make the groups of digits as shown below. Put them in the spaces on the Reading Millions Frame below to read them.

28,374	654,321	92,148	789,321
1,000,000	34,185,726	20,090,870	707,005,009

Reading Millions Frame

millions   thousands   [ones]

Read and Write Expanded Form

Read and write each number in expanded form.

1 32,568 _____

2 820,149 _____

3 405,763 _____

4 703,070 _____

Read and write each number in standard form.

5 20,000 + 4,000 + 800 + 10 + 7 _____

6 700,000 + 50,000 + 3,000 + 200 + 90 + 6 _____

7 300,000 + 3,000 + 10 + 9 _____

8 800,000 + 40,000 + 400 + 80 _____

Read and write each number in word form.

9 90,000 + 7,000 + 300 + 20 + 4 _____

10 600,000 + 30,000 + 4,000 + 700 + 30 _____

11 200,000 + 3,000 + 80 + 6 _____

12 500,000 + 20,000 + 400 + 1 _____

Read and write each number in standard form.

13 seventy-eight thousand, one hundred five _____

14 one million _____

15 five hundred sixty-three thousand, fifty-two _____

✓ **Check Understanding**

Describe the role of a comma when reading and writing multidigit whole numbers.

Numbers to One Million

Name _____

Compare Greater Numbers

Discuss the problem below.

A stadium hosted both a concert and a sporting event.
The concert had 101,835 people in attendance.
The sporting event had 101,538 people in attendance.
Which event had more people in attendance?
How do you know?

Compare. Write >, <, or = to make each statement true.

1 12,563 ⊙> 11,987   **2** 14,615 ⊙< 15,651

3 23,487 ⊙< 28,734   **4** 83,342 ⊙> 80,423

5 79,131 ⊙> 79,113   **6** 126,348 ⊙< 162,634

7 705,126 ⊙= 705,126   **8** 532,834 ⊙< 532,843

9 647,313 ⊙> 647,310   **10** 198,593 ⊙> 98,593

11 75,621 ⊙> 705,126   **12** 1,000,000 ⊙> 100,000

Greatest Place Value

Round to the (nearest) ten thousand. (to the)

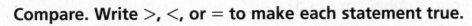

13 25,987 __3,000__
    3̶0̶,̶0̶0̶0̶   **14** 13,738 __4,000__   **15** 48,333 __50,000__

16 84,562 __8,000__   **17** 92,132 __9,000__   **18** 99,141 __100000__

Round to the nearest hundred thousand.

19 531,987 __5,000__   **20** 701,828 __1,000__

21 670,019 __$7,000__   **22** 249,845 __2,000__

23 390,101 __4,000__   **24** 999,999 __100000__

Round to Any Place

Solve.

25 Write a number that changes to 310,000 when it is rounded. To what place was your number rounded?

_____

26 Write a number that changes to 901,400 when it is rounded. To what place was your number rounded?

_____

27 Write a number that changes to 800,000 when it is rounded. To what place was your number rounded?

_____

28 Write a number that changes to 122,000 when it is rounded. To what place was your number rounded?

_____

29 What is 395,101 rounded to the nearest:

a. ten? _____

b. hundred? _____

c. thousand? _____

d. ten thousand? _____

e. hundred thousand? _____

30 What is 958,069 rounded to the nearest:

a. ten? _____

b. hundred? _____

c. thousand? _____

d. ten thousand? _____

e. hundred thousand? _____

Check Understanding

Round 465,345 to the ten thousands place. Then compare the rounded number to the original number using the symbols $>$, $<$, or $=$.

_____

Compare and Round Greater Numbers

Name _____

Discuss Different Methods

Discuss how each addition method can be used to add 4-digit numbers.

$$5,879 + 6,754$$

1 New Groups Above Method

Step 1	Step 2	Step 3	Step 4
¹ 5,879	¹ ¹ 5,879	¹ ¹ ¹ 5,879	¹ ¹ ¹ 5,879
+ 6,754	+ 6,754	+ 6,754	+ 6,754
3	33	633	12,633

2 New Groups Below Method

Step 1	Step 2	Step 3	Step 4
5,879	5,879	5,879	5,879
+ 6,754	+ 6,754	+ 6,754	+ 6,754
₁ 3	₁ ₁ 33	₁ ₁ ₁ 633	₁ ₁ ₁ 12,633

3 Show Subtotals Method (Right-to-Left)

Step 1	Step 2	Step 3	Step 4	Step 5
5,879	5,879	5,879	5,879	5,879
+ 6,754	+ 6,754	+ 6,754	+ 6,754	+ 6,754
13	13	13	13	13
	120	120	120	120
		1,500	1,500	1,500
			11,000	11,000
				+ 11,000
				12,633

PATH to FLUENCY Practice

4 908
     + 653

5 692
     + 543

6 5,362
     + 3,746

7 3,786
     + 6,335

PATH to FLUENCY Practice (continued)

8 2,782
    + 5,246

9 6,293
    + 3,862

10 3,729
     + 4,541

11 8,196
     + 3,865

12 7,862
     + 2,839

13 2,764
     + 6,648

14 4,825
     + 2,467

15 5,364
     + 4,754

Addition and Money

Think about how to solve this problem.

Carlos is saving money to buy a skateboard. He saved $27 one week and $14 the next week. How much did Carlos save altogether? _____

Solve each problem.

16 Robyn's grandmother gave her $38 for her birthday and her uncle gave her $25. How much did Robyn get altogether?

_____

17 A parent-teacher club sold baked goods to raise money for the school. They collected $268 on Friday and $479 on Saturday. How much did they collect altogether?

_____

✔**Check Understanding**

Explain how you know when to make a new group in addition.

Make New Groups for Addition

Name _____

Use Estimation

You can use rounding to estimate a total. Then you can adjust your estimated total to find the exact total.

The best-selling fruits at Joy's Fruit Shack are peaches and bananas. During one month Joy sold 397 peaches and 412 bananas.

$0.60 $0.65

1. *About* how many peaches and bananas did she sell in all?

    809   397

2. *Exactly* how many peaches and bananas did she sell?

    397 peaches + 412 bananas = 809 fruits $\dfrac{412}{809}$

Estimate. Then adjust your estimate to find the exact answer.

3. 89 + 28

4. 153 + 98

5. 1,297 + 802

6. 1,066 + 45,104

Solve.

Show your work.

Tomás has $100. He wants to buy a $38 jacket. He also wants to buy a $49 pair of shoes and 2 ties that are on sale 2 for $8.

7. How can Tomás figure out whether he has enough money for all four items? Does he have enough?

    _____

    _____

Use Estimation (continued)

Show your work.

Students at Washington Middle School collected 1,598 cans during the first month of their aluminum drive. During the second month of the drive, they collected 2,006 cans.

$$
\begin{array}{r}
\overset{1\ 1}{1,598} \\
+\ 2,006 \\
\hline
=3,604
\end{array}
$$

8 About how many cans did the students collect in all?

I think mabye about 4,000

9 Exactly how many cans did the students collect in all?

They collected 3,604 in total.

Look for "Easy" Combinations

You can sometimes find number combinations that make it possible to add numbers mentally.

10 Add 243, 274, 252, and 231 vertically.

11 Explain how you can use number combinations to help you add the numbers.

You can yk use sub todal or bring it below, briny it above.

Share Solutions

Find the total. Add mentally if you can.

12
$$
\begin{array}{r}
8 \\
4 \\
6 \\
+\ 2 \\
\hline
20
\end{array}
$$

13
$$
\begin{array}{r}
46 \\
21 \\
+\ 64 \\
\hline
131
\end{array}
$$

14
$$
\begin{array}{r}
35 \\
29 \\
75 \\
+\ 61 \\
\hline
200
\end{array}
$$

15
$$
\begin{array}{r}
348 \\
516 \\
+\ 492 \\
\hline
1356
\end{array}
$$

16
$$
\begin{array}{r}
147 \\
182 \\
108 \\
+\ 165 \\
\hline
6\ 02
\end{array}
$$

✓ Check Understanding

Find an estimate and the exact total.

$37 + 96 + 104 + 64$

Estimate: _____   Exact total: _____

Estimation and Mental Math

Family Letter | Content Overview

Dear Family:

Your child is now learning about subtraction. A common subtraction mistake is subtracting in the wrong direction. Children may think that they always subtract the smaller digit from the larger digit, but this is not true. To help children avoid this mistake, the *Math Expressions* program encourages children to "fix" numbers first and then subtract.

When one or more digits in the top number are smaller than the corresponding digits in the bottom number, fix the numbers by "ungrouping." For example, 1,634 − 158 is shown below:

1. We cannot subtract 8 ones from 4 ones. We get more ones by ungrouping 1 ten to make 10 ones.

We now have 14 ones and only 2 tens.

$$\begin{array}{r} {}^{2\,14} \\ 1,6\,\cancel{3}\,\cancel{4} \\ -\ \ 1\,5\,8 \\ \hline \end{array}$$

2. We cannot subtract 5 tens from 2 tens. We get more tens by ungrouping 1 hundred to make 10 tens.

We now have 12 tens and only 5 hundreds.

$$\begin{array}{r} {}^{12} \\ {}^{5\,\cancel{2}14} \\ 1,\cancel{6}\,\cancel{3}4 \\ -\ \ 1\,5\,8 \\ \hline \end{array}$$

3. Now we can subtract:
1 − 0 = 1 thousand
5 − 1 = 4 hundreds
12 − 5 = 7 tens
14 − 8 = 6 ones

$$\begin{array}{r} {}^{12} \\ {}^{5\,\cancel{2}14} \\ 1,\cancel{6}\,\cancel{3}\cancel{4} \\ -\ \ 1\,5\,8 \\ \hline 1,4\,7\,6 \end{array}$$

In the method above, the numbers are ungrouped from right to left, but students can also ungroup from left to right. Children can choose whichever way works best for them.

The unit concludes with opportunities to review and practice basic multiplications and divisions by using multiplication tables, product cards, and games. Exploring patterns, such as 4s, 6s, 8s, and 10s products as doubles of 2s, 3s, 4s, and 5s products, helps build fluency.

$6 \times \underline{2} = 12$ $6 \times \underline{4} = 24$

$6 \times \underline{3} = 18$ $6 \times \underline{6} = 36$

$6 \times \underline{4} = 24$ $6 \times \underline{8} = 48$

$6 \times \underline{5} = 30$ $6 \times \underline{10} = 60$

Your child should also continue to practice multiplication and division skills at home.

If you have any questions or comments, please contact me.

Sincerely,
Your child's teacher

Estimada familia:

Ahora su niño está aprendiendo a restar. Un error muy común al restar, es hacerlo en la dirección equivocada. Los niños pueden pensar que siempre se resta el dígito más pequeño del dígito más grande, pero no es verdad. Para ayudar a los niños a no cometer este error, el programa *Math Expressions* les propone "arreglar" los números primero y luego restar.

Cuando uno o más dígitos del número de arriba son más pequeños que los dígitos correspondientes del número de abajo, se arreglan los números "desagrupándolos". Por ejemplo, 1,634 − 158 se muestra abajo:

1. No podemos restar 8 unidades de 4 unidades. Obtenemos más unidades al desagrupar 1 decena para formar 10 unidades.

Ahora tenemos 14 unidades y solamente 2 decenas.

$$\begin{array}{r} {\scriptstyle 2\,14} \\ 1,6\,\cancel{3}\,\cancel{4} \\ -\ \ 1\,5\,8 \\ \hline \end{array}$$

2. No podemos restar 5 decenas de 2 decenas. Obtenemos más decenas al desagrupar 1 centena para formar 10 decenas.

Ahora tenemos 12 decenas y solamente 5 centenas.

$$\begin{array}{r} {\scriptstyle 12} \\ {\scriptstyle 5\,\cancel{2}\,14} \\ 1,\cancel{6}\,\cancel{3}\,\cancel{4} \\ -\ \ 1\,5\,8 \\ \hline \end{array}$$

3. Ahora podemos restar:

1 − 0 = 1 millar
5 − 1 = 4 centenas
12 − 5 = 7 decenas
14 − 8 = 6 unidades

$$\begin{array}{r} {\scriptstyle 12} \\ {\scriptstyle 5\,\cancel{2}\,14} \\ 1,\cancel{6}\,\cancel{3}\,\cancel{4} \\ -\ \ 1\,5\,8 \\ \hline 1,4\,7\,6 \end{array}$$

En el método de arriba se desagrupan los números de derecha a izquierda, pero también se pueden desagrupar de izquierda a derecha. Los niños pueden escoger la manera que les resulte más fácil.

La unidad concluye con la oportunidad de revisar y practicar multiplicaciones y divisiones básicas usando tablas de multiplicación, tarjetas de productos y juegos. Explorar patrones, tales como 4, 6, 8 y 10 productos dobles de 2, 3, 4 y 5, ayuda a desarrollar la fluidez.

6 × <u>2</u> = 12	6 × <u>4</u> = 24
6 × <u>3</u> = 18	6 × <u>6</u> = 36
6 × <u>4</u> = 24	6 × <u>8</u> = 48
6 × <u>5</u> = 30	6 × <u>10</u> = 60

Su niño también debe seguir practicando las destrezas de multiplicación y de división en casa.

Si tiene alguna pregunta, por favor comuníquese conmigo.

Atentamente,
El maestro de su niño

Name Sidra Saeed

Discuss Ungrouping With Zeros

Look inside the magnifying glass and discuss each
ungrouping step.

1 Ungroup step-by-step: *or*   **2** Ungroup all at once:

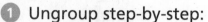

$$\begin{array}{r} {}^{9\ 9}\\ {}^{7\ 10\ 10\ 10}\\ 8\,0\,0\,0\\ -\ 3{,}4\,9\,2\\ \hline \end{array} \qquad \begin{array}{r} {}^{7\ 9\ 9\ 10}\\ 8\,0\,0\,0\\ -\ 3{,}4\,9\,2\\ \hline \end{array}$$

Decide When to Ungroup

3 Ungroup left-to-right: *or*   **4** Ungroup right-to-left:

$$\begin{array}{r} {}^{15\ 11}\\ {}^{3\ 16\ 12\ 15}\\ 4\,6\,2\,5\\ -\ 2{,}9\,8\,7\\ \hline \end{array} \qquad \begin{array}{r} {}^{15\ 11}\\ {}^{3\ 16\ 12\ 15}\\ 4\,6\,2\,5\\ -\ 2{,}9\,8\,7\\ \hline \end{array}$$

Other Ungrouping Situations

5 When we have zeros and other
digits on the top:

$$\begin{array}{r} {}^{1\ 16\ 9\ 13}\\ {}^{8\ 10}\\ 2\,7\,0\,3\\ -\ 1{,}9\,6\,6\\ \hline \end{array}$$

6 When we have the same digit
on the top and bottom:

$$\begin{array}{r} {}^{13\ 17}\\ {}^{4\ 14\ 7\ 13}\\ 5\,4\,8\,3\\ -\ 1{,}6\,8\,7\\ \hline \end{array}$$

Solve and Discuss

Subtract. Show your new groups.

7
$$\begin{array}{r} {}^{9\ 9\ 9}\\ 7\,8{,}0\,0\,0\ {}^{10}\\ -\ 1{,}6\,9\,1\\ \hline 6\,3\,0\,4\ \checkmark \end{array}$$

8
$$\begin{array}{r} {}^{13\ 1}\\ {}^{18\ 17}\\ {}^{14\ 16}\\ 8\,9{,}4\,6\,2\ {}^{20}\\ -\ 5{,}6\,7\,8\\ \hline 3\,9\,8\,9\ \checkmark \end{array}$$

9
$$\begin{array}{r} 6{,}3\,4\,5\\ -\ 2{,}3\,5\,6\\ \hline \end{array}$$

© Houghton Mifflin Harcourt Publishing Company

PATH to FLUENCY Practice

Subtract. Show your new groups.

10. $\begin{array}{r} {}^{8}7,919 \\ -\ 3,846 \\ \hline \end{array}$ 4073

11. $\begin{array}{r} {}^{149}_{150}\ 7\ 8,502\ 12 \\ -\ 3,749 \\ \hline \end{array}$ 4,753

12. $\begin{array}{r} 4,221 \\ -\ 2,805 \\ \hline \end{array}$ 1406

13. $\begin{array}{r} 7,000 \\ -\ \ \ 572 \\ \hline \end{array}$ 6,428

14. $\begin{array}{r} 4,650 \\ -\ 2,793 \\ \hline \end{array}$ 2,057

15. $\begin{array}{r} 4,605 \\ -\ 1,711 \\ \hline \end{array}$ 2899

16. $\begin{array}{r} 3,120 \\ -\ \ \ \ 38 \\ \hline \end{array}$ 3082

17. $\begin{array}{r} 6,082 \\ -\ \ \ \ 95 \\ \hline \end{array}$ 3987

18. $\begin{array}{r} 2,107 \\ -\ \ \ 428 \\ \hline \end{array}$

19. $\begin{array}{r} 1,852 \\ -\ \ \ 964 \\ \hline \end{array}$

20. $\begin{array}{r} 3,692 \\ -\ 2,704 \\ \hline \end{array}$

21. $\begin{array}{r} 8,715 \\ -\ 6,742 \\ \hline \end{array}$

22. $\begin{array}{r} 6,000 \\ -\ 4,351 \\ \hline \end{array}$

23. $\begin{array}{r} 7,400 \\ -\ 1,215 \\ \hline \end{array}$

24. $\begin{array}{r} 3,583 \\ -\ 1,794 \\ \hline \end{array}$

Solve.

25. Jake has 647 pennies in his penny collection album. The album has space for 1,000 pennies. How many more pennies can Jake place in his album?

_____

26. A ship is making an 8,509-mile voyage. So far, it has sailed 2,957 miles. How many miles of the voyage remain?

_____

✔ Check Understanding

Describe how to use ungrouping to subtract from thousands.

Subtract From Thousands

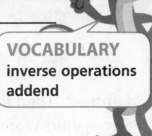

Relate Addition to Subtraction

Addition and subtraction are **inverse operations.**
Break-apart drawings help to show inverse relationships.

1 Write a word problem that requires adding 1,310
and 2,057.

_____

_____

_____

_____

2 Write the **addends** and the sum in the break-apart
drawing.

3 Complete the two addition problems represented by
the break-apart drawing.

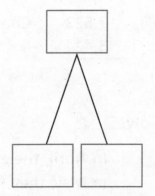

$$\begin{array}{r} 1,310 \\ +\underline{\hphantom{0000}} \\ 3,367 \end{array} \qquad \begin{array}{r} 2,057 \\ +\underline{\hphantom{0000}} \\ \underline{\hphantom{0000}} \end{array}$$

4 Write a word problem that requires subtracting 1,310
from 3,367.

_____

_____

_____

_____

5 Write two subtraction exercises represented by the
break-apart drawing.

(PATH to FLUENCY) Practice

Subtract. Then use addition to check the subtraction.
Show your work.

6
$$\begin{array}{r} 1\ 89 \\ 0\cancel{1,900}^{10} \\ -\ 0\ 574 \\ \hline 1,826 \end{array}$$

Check:
$$\begin{array}{r} 1 \\ 1,900 \\ +\ 574 \\ \hline 2,474 \end{array}$$

7
$$\begin{array}{r} 7 \\ 1,800 \\ -\ 1,216 \\ \hline \end{array}$$
Check:

8
$$\begin{array}{r} 4\ ^{11}5,192 \\ -\quad 341 \\ \hline 4,851 \end{array}$$

Check:
$$\begin{array}{r} + \\ 5,192 \\ +\ 0\ 341 \\ \hline 5,523 \end{array}$$

9
$$\begin{array}{r} 6,350 \\ -\ 2,460 \\ \hline \end{array}$$
Check:

10
$$\begin{array}{r} 7,523 \\ -\ 3,424 \\ \hline \end{array}$$

Check:
$$\begin{array}{r} 7,523 \\ +\ 3,424 \\ \hline \end{array}$$

11
$$\begin{array}{r} 2,000 \\ -\quad 651 \\ \hline \end{array}$$
Check:

Solve.

12 a. In April, the zookeepers fed the penguins 4,620 fish.
In May, they fed the penguins 5,068 fish. How many
fish did they feed the penguins altogether?

_____

b. Suppose the head keeper knows the total number
of fish fed to the penguins in April and May, and
knows the penguins were fed 4,620 fish in April.
Show how the keeper can use subtraction to find
the number of fish the penguins were fed in May.
(Use your answer from Part a.)

_____

✓ **Check Understanding**
Describe the relationship between addition and
subtraction. Give examples of related problems.

Subtraction Undoes Addition

Name Sidra Saeed, Monatha

Find and Correct Mistakes

Always check your work. Many mistakes can be easily fixed.

**What is the mistake in each problem? How can you fix
the mistake and find the correct answer?**

1 67,308 − 5,497

$$
\begin{array}{r}
6\,\overset{6}{7}\,\overset{12}{3}\,\overset{13}{0}\,\overset{10}{8} \\
-\ 5,4\,9\,7\,0 \\
\hline
1\,2,3\,3\,8 \checkmark
\end{array}
$$

2 134,865 − 5,294

$$
\begin{array}{r}
1\,3\,4,8\,6\,5 \\
-\ \ \ \ 5,2\,9\,4 \\
\hline
1\,3\,1,6\,3\,1
\end{array}
$$

The mistake was that they made the 700 in to a six hund even though they could subtract. And the 5 is sapoest to be in the thousand.

They should have regroup. Also or another way to say that they should have regrouped the hund into the tens. ☺

Check Subtraction by "Adding Up"

"Add up" to find any places where there is a subtraction
mistake. Discuss how each mistake might have been
made and correct the subtraction if necessary.

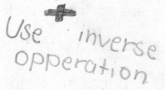
Use + inverse opperation

3
$$
\begin{array}{r}
163,406 \\
-\ 84,357 \\
\hline
79,159
\end{array}
$$
Aser:

4
$$
\begin{array}{r}
526,741 \\
-\ 139,268 \\
\hline
413,473
\end{array}
$$

5
$$
\begin{array}{r}
1,000,000 \\
-\ 300,128 \\
\hline
600,872
\end{array}
$$

6
$$
\begin{array}{r}
5,472,639 \\
-\ 2,375,841 \\
\hline
3,096,798
\end{array}
$$

7 Write and solve a subtraction problem with numbers in
the hundred thousands.

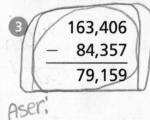

$$
\begin{array}{r}
472,9\,2\,8 \\
-\ 641,9\,2\,4 \\
\hline
09
\end{array}
$$

Reasonable

Estimate Differences   This is what I remeber!

You can use estimation to decide if an answer is reasonable.

Dan did this subtraction: 8,196 − 5,980. His answer was
3,816. Discuss how using estimation can help you decide
if his answer is correct.

Decide whether each answer is reasonable. Show your estimate.

8 4,914 − 949 = 3,065

4,000

Stop

9 52,022 − 29,571 = 22,451

22 451

5,000 29,000 22,000

Solve.

Show your work.

10 Bob has 3,226 marbles in his collection. Mia has 1,867
marbles. Bob says he has 2,359 more than Mia. Is Bob's
answer reasonable? Show your estimate.

11 Two towns have populations of 24,990 and 12,205.
Gretchen says the difference is 12,785. Is Gretchen's
answer reasonable? Show your estimate.

25,000 − 12,000 = 43,000

12 Estimate to decide if the answer is
reasonable. If it is not reasonable,
describe the mistake and find the
correct answer.

$$\begin{array}{r} 805,716 \\ -\ 290,905 \\ \hline 614,811 \end{array}$$

Check Understanding

Describe how subtracting and ungrouping with greater
numbers is similar to subtracting and ungrouping with
lesser numbers.

Subtract Greater Numbers

© Houghton Mifflin Harcourt Publishing Company

Discuss the Steps of the Problem

Sometimes you will need to work through more than one step to solve a problem. The steps can be shown in one or more equations.

1 In the morning, 19 students were working on a science project. In the afternoon, 3 students left and 7 more students came to work on the project. How many students were working on the project at the end of the day?

_____

2 Solve the problem again by finishing Anita's and Chad's methods. Then discuss what is alike and what is different about each method.

Anita's Method	Chad's Method
Write an equation for each step.	**Write an equation for the whole problem.**
Find the total number of students who worked on the project.	Let $n =$ the number of students working on the project at the end of the day.
$19 + 7 =$ ___	Students who left in the afternoon. Students who arrived in the afternoon.
Subtract the number of students who left in the afternoon.	$19 -$ ___ $+$ ___ $= n$
$26 - 3 =$ ___	___ $= n$

3 Solve. Discuss the steps you used.

A team is scheduled to play 12 games. Of those games, 7 will be played at home. The other games are away games. How many fewer away games than home games will be played?

_____

_____

Share Solutions

Solve each problem.

Show your work.

4 The school library has ⟨288⟩ science books. ⟨Altogether⟩ the library has 618 science and animal books. How many fewer science books than animal books does the library have?

$$288 + X = 618 \text{ so } 618 - 288 = 330 \text{ fewer}$$

5 6̸1̸8
 288
――――
 330

5 Olivia's stamp collection consists of ⟨442⟩ stamps. There are ⟨131⟩ animal stamps and ⟨107⟩ famous people stamps in her collection. How many of Olivia's stamps are not of animals or famous people?

$$107 - 131 = X_3 = \boxed{24}$$

P	A	T
107	131	442

2 3̸7̸10
  288
――――
 0̸4 2

024

PATH to FLUENCY **Practice Multidigit Addition and Subtraction**

6
```
    985
  − 792
```

7
```
   2,931
 + 8,563
```

8
```
   4,201
 + 9,979
```

9
```
   98,309
 − 48,659
```

10
```
   78,196
 − 14,587
```

11
```
   21,682
 + 95,436
```

12
```
   373,095
 + 185,543
```

13
```
   709,032
 − 239,125
```

14
```
   540,721
 + 375,699
```

✓ **Check Understanding**

Describe how to solve two-step problems.

Practice Addition and Subtraction

Discuss Problem Types

Think of different types of problems for each exercise.
Write an equation for the problem then solve it.

O
1 $a + 278 = 747$

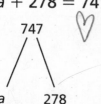

747
/ \
a   278

$747 - 278 = 489$
 489

E
2 $b - 346 = 587$

b
/ \
346   587

$346 + 587 =$

O
3 933

933
/ \
c   346

$933 - 346 =$

400
200   700

E
4

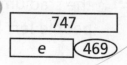

| 747 |
| e | 469 |

PATH to FLUENCY **Share Solutions**

Write an equation for the problem then solve it.
Make a math drawing if you need to.

Show your work.

O
5 Of 800,000 species of insects, about 560,000 undergo complete metamorphosis. How many species do not undergo complete metamorphosis?

6 800,000 −
  560,000   Species
              140,000
=140,000

800,000
/ \
800   a   560,000

6 The Great Pyramid of Giza has about 2,000,000 stone blocks. A replica has 1,900,000 fewer blocks. How many blocks are in the replica?

12,000,000 = 0,100,000
 1,900,000   100,000 are in Replica
00,100,000

7 Last year 439,508 people visited the science museum. This is 46,739 fewer visitors than this year. How many people visited the science museum this year?

439,508
739,

PATH to FLUENCY Share Solutions (continued)

Show your work.

8 At the end of a baseball game, there were 35,602 people in the stadium. There were 37,614 people in the stadium at the beginning of the game. How many people left before the game ended?

_____

_____

9 This year Pinnacle Publishing printed 64,924 more books than Premier Publishing. If Pinnacle printed 231,069 books, how many books did Premier print?

_____

_____

10 Mary drove her car 2,483 miles during a road trip. Now she has 86,445 miles on her car. How many miles did her car have before her trip?

_____

_____

11 The Yellow River in China is 5,465 kilometers long. It is 4,295 kilometers longer than the Elbe River in Europe. How long is the Elbe River?

_____

_____

12 A bridge is 1,595 feet long. Each cable holding up the bridge is 1,983 feet longer than the bridge itself. How long is each cable?

_____

_____

　　Problem Solving With Greater Numbers

Subtraction and Money

Sondra had $140 to spend on new clothes for school. She bought a shirt for $21. You can use a model to help you find out how much money she has left.

Sondra had _____ left.

Solve each problem. Use money if you need to.

Show your work.

13 Jason had $30. He gave $18 to his brother. How much money does Jason have left?

_____

14 Elana's coach had some money to spend on softball equipment. She spent $76 on bases. She has $174 left. How much did she have to start?

_____

15 The school science club raised $325. After buying equipment for an experiment they had $168 left. How much did they spend?

_____

16 Amy's family has a budget of $850 for buying new furniture. They buy a couch for $575. How much is left in their furniture budget?

_____

© Houghton Mifflin Harcourt Publishing Company

Determine Reasonable Answers

Solve each problem. Check your answers using inverse operations.

⑰ Mrs. Washington has $265. She wants to buy shoes for $67 and dresses for $184. Does she have enough money? Explain your answer. _516 25(_

(handwritten: 2 1 / 265 / 1 8 4 / 6 7 / 516)

⑱ Terrell wants to run at least 105 miles during the month. He ran a total of 87 miles during the first 3 weeks of the month. If he runs 25 miles in the fourth week, will he make his goal? Explain. _____

(handwritten: 87 / +25 / 11 2)

What's the Error?

(handwritten: be will mak a big goal)

Dear Math Students,

My friend is taking a trip to Antarctica. He gave me $112 to buy him some clothes. I tried to buy a parka and two pairs of wool socks, but the clerk said I didn't have enough money. I added the cost like this:

$98 + $12 = $110

Can you help me figure out what I did wrong?

Your friend,
Puzzled Penguin

Bill's Outdoor Wear

Pair of wool socks	$12
Hat	$15
Mittens	$10
Parka	$98

⑲ Write a response to Puzzled Penguin.
First add 12+12 for wool socks. and its 24.
And add 98.

✔ **Check Understanding**

If Puzzled Penguin wanted to buy a parka and a hat, what would the total be? _____ Does Puzzled Penguin have enough money? _____

Problem Solving With Greater Numbers

Make a Bar Graph

Bridges are structures that are built to get over obstacles like water, a valley, or roads. Bridges can be made of concrete, steel, or even tree roots. Engineers and designers do a lot of math to be sure a bridge will stand up to its use and the forces of nature that affect it.

Lengths of Bridges		
Bridge	**Length Over Water (ft)**	Round to thousan
Manchac Swamp Bridge, U.S.A.	121,440	121,000
Hangzhou Bay Bridge, China	117,057	117,000
Lake Pontchartrain Causeway, U.S.A.	125,664	126,000
Jiaozhou Bay Bridge, China	139,392	139,000

1 Use the data in the table above to make a bar graph.

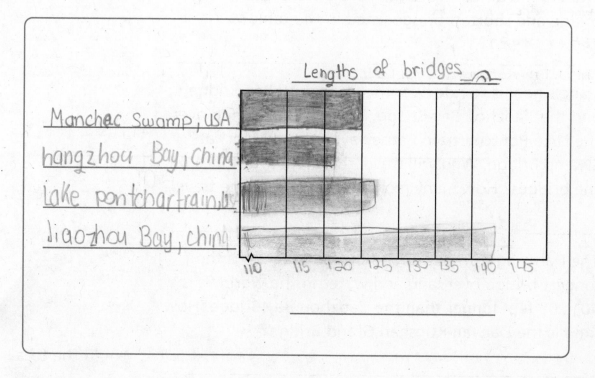

Add and Subtract Greater Numbers

The Lake Pontchartrain Causeway is composed of two parallel bridges crossing Lake Pontchartrain in Louisiana. It is the longest bridge in the United States.

For Problems 2–5, use the data in the table on page 41.

Show your work.

2 How much longer is the Lake Pontchartrain Causeway than the Hangzhou Bay Bridge?

If you subtract 125,604 and 117,057 you should get 8,547

$$
\begin{array}{r}
125,604 \\
- 117,057 \\
\hline
008,547
\end{array}
$$

3 What is the difference in length between the longest bridge and shortest bridge listed in the table?

If the longest bridge is 139,000 and the smallest one is only 117,057 so all I did was subtract and got 041,943

$$
\begin{array}{r}
139,000 \\
- 117,057 \\
\hline
041,943
\end{array}
$$

4 Liang's goal is to ride over the Hangzhou Bay Bridge and the Jiaozhou Bay Bridge. Tanya wants to ride over the Lake Pontchartrain Causeway and the Manchac Swamp Bridge. Who will travel the greater distance on the bridges? How many more feet will he or she travel?

125,604
121,440
247,104
247,104

104 247,104

117,057
117,057
+139,092

5 The Danyang-Kunshan Grand Bridge in China is the longest bridge over land and water in the world. It is 401,308 feet longer than the Jiaozhou Bay Bridge. How long is the Danyan-Kunshan Grand Bridge?

156,449

Focus on Problem Solving

Subtract.

① 409,867
  − 377,294
  _____

Solve.

Show your work.

② Most tickets were sold before Sunday. On Sunday 9,854 more tickets are sold. 92,563 tickets were sold in all. How many tickets were sold before Sunday?

_____

③ Earth has an average diameter of about 7,926 miles. Mercury's approximate average diameter is 4,894 miles less than Earth's. What is Mercury's average diameter?

_____

④ Lance's class read for a total of 7,842 minutes during a read-a-thon. Alex's class read for 9,310 minutes. Alex wrote this subtraction equation to show how many more minutes his class read than Lance's class.

$$9,310 - 7,842 = \blacksquare$$

Solve Alex's equation and write an addition equation to check the subtraction.

_____

Write an equation and solve the problem.

⑤ Chris scored 34,809 points in one computer game. He scored 6,250 fewer points in another game. How many points did Chris score in both games?

_____

_____

Name _____ Date _____

Add or subtract.

1   303
    + 251

2   9,208
    − 5,107

3   32,971
    + 4,643

4   35,977
    + 41,682

5   301,429
    − 78,046

6   448,054
    + 209,186

7   437
    + 259

8   89,307
    − 6,346

9   695
    − 542

10 7,293
    +   561

11 5,259
    − 1,739

12 791
    − 438

13 2,786
    + 1,433

14 76,176
    − 46,233

15 542,711
    − 358,525

Name Sidra Saeed Monatha

VOCABULARY
factor
product

(PATH to FLUENCY) Complete a Multiplication Table

1 Look at the **factors** to complete the Multiplication Table. Leave blanks for the **products** you do not know.

FACTORS

×	1	2	3	4	5	6	7	8	9	10
1	1	2	3	4	5	6	7	8	9	10
2	2	4	6	8	10	12	14	16	18	20
3	3	6	9	12	15	18	21	24	27	30
4	4	8	12	16	20	24	28	22	36	40
5	5	10	15	20	25	30	35	40	43	50
6	6	12	18	24	30	36	40	45	45	60
7	7	14	27	28	30	35	42	48	ω	70
8	8	16	24	32	40	42	56	72	70	80
9	9	18	27	36	45	56 63	63	83	81	90
10	10	20	30	40	50	63 60	70	80	90	1000

2 Write the multiplications you need to practice.

_____

_____

_____

_____

Build Fluency with Multiplication and Division **45**

PATH to FLUENCY Scrambled Multiplication Tables $9 \times 7 =$

Complete each table.

A

×	1	5	9	10	7	4	3	2	8	6
6	6	30	54	60	42	24	18	12	48	36
2	2	10	18	20	14	8	6	4	16	12
10	10	50	90	100	70	40	30	20	80	60
8	8	40	72	80	56	32	24	16	64	48
5	5	25	45	50	35	20	15	10	40	30
1	1	5	9	10	7	4	3	2	8	6
9	9	45	81	90	63	36	27	18	72	54
4	4	20	36	40	28	16	12	8	32	24
7	7	35	63	70	49	28	21	14	56	42
3	3	15	27	30	21	12	9	6	24	18

B

×	10	3	2	4	7	5	6	9	8	1
10	100	30	20	40	70	50		90	80	10
5	50	15	10	20	35	25	30	45	40	5
1	10	3	2	4	7	5	6	9	8	1
3	30	9	6	12	21	15	R	27	24	3
2	20	6	4	8	14	10	12	18	16	2
4	40	12	8	16	28	20		36	32	4
9	90	27	18	36	63	45	54	81	72	9
6	60	18	12	24		30	36	54	48	6
7	70	21	14	28	49	35	42	61	56	7
8	80	24	16	32	56	40		72	64	8

Factors

C

×	9	2	8	7	6	5	4	3	1	10
3	27	6	24	21	18	15	12	9	3	30
4	36	8	32	28	24	20	16	12	4	40
1	9	2	8	7	6	5	4	3	1	10
2	18	4	16	14	30	10	8	6	2	20
7	63	14	56	49	42	35	28	21	7	10
8	72	16	64	56	48	40	32	24	8	80
5	45	10	40	35	30	25	20	15	5	50
6	54	12	48	42	36	30	24	18	6	60
10	90	20	80	70	60	50	40	30	10	100
9	81	18	72	63	54	45	36	27	9	1,000

factors

D

×	8	4	7	2	6	10	3	1	9	5
6	48	24	42	12	36	60	18	6	54	30
7	56	28	49	14	42	70	21	7	63	35
10	80	40	70	20	60	100	30	10	40	50
5	45	20	35	10	30	50	15	5	45	25
4	32	16	28	8	24	40	12	4	36	20
1	8	4	7	2	6	10	3	1	9	5
2	16	8	14	4	12	20	6	2	18	10
8	64	32	56	16	48	80	24	8	72	40
9	72	36	63	18			27		81	
3	24		21		18	30		3	27	

✔ Check Understanding

Complete the sentences. Factors $F \times F = P$

The numbers in the yellow boxes are ___yellow___.

The numbers in the white boxes are ___products___.

Build Fluency with Multiplication and Division

Name Sidra Saeed

PATH to FLUENCY Patterns with 10s, 5s, and 9s

These multiplication tables help us see some patterns
that make recalling basic multiplications easier.

1 What pattern do you see in the
10s count-bys?

Digit in the ones place

<u>I can see the 10's patern.</u>
10, 20, 30, 40, 50, 60, 70, 80, 90, 100

2 Look at the 5s and the 10s together.
What patterns do you see? *10s*

<u>I see that in the 10s pattern</u>
<u>there are 5 more then the 5.</u>

0 and 5

5s and 10s

×	1	2	3	4	5	6	7	8	9	10
1	1	2	3	4	5	6	7	8	9	10
2	2	4	6	8	10	12	14	16	18	20
3	3	6	9	12	15	18	21	24	27	30
4	4	8	12	16	20	24	28	32	36	40
5	5	10	15	20	25	30	35	40	45	50
6	6	12	18	24	30	36	42	48	54	60
7	7	14	21	28	35	42	49	56	63	70
8	8	16	24	32	40	48	56	64	72	80
9	9	18	27	36	45	54	63	72	81	90
10	10	20	30	40	50	60	70	80	90	100

3 Look at the 9s count-bys. How does
each 9s count-by relate to the
10s count-by in the next row?

<u>There 2 away</u>

How could this pattern help you
remember the 9s count-bys?

<u>I could remeber it becanse it shows</u>
<u>9+9+9+9+9 and keeps going.</u>

9s

×	1	2	3	4	5	6	7	8	9	10
1	1	2	3	4	5	6	7	8	9	10
2	2	4	6	8	10	12	14	16	18	20
3	3	6	9	12	15	18	21	24	27	30
4	4	8	12	16	20	24	28	32	36	40
5	5	10	15	20	25	30	35	40	45	50
6	6	12	18	24	30	36	42	48	54	60
7	7	14	21	28	35	42	49	56	63	70
8	8	16	24	32	40	48	56	64	72	80
9	9	18	27	36	45	54	63	72	81	90
10	10	20	30	40	50	60	70	80	90	100

4 Look at the digits in each 9s product.
What is the sum of the digits in each
9s product?

<u>its by 1's (it think)?</u>

How could you use this knowledge to check
your answers when you multiply by 9?

Multiplication Patterns **47**

(PATH to FLUENCY) **Patterns with Other Numbers**

On the multiplication table, find patterns with 2s, 4s, 6s, and 8s.

5 Look at the ones digits in all the 2s, 4s, 6s, and 8s count-bys. What pattern do you see?

there the same numbers

6 Are the 2s, 4s, 6s, and 8s products even numbers or odd numbers?

even numbers

2s, 4s, 6s, 8s

×	1	2	3	4	5	6	7	8	9	10
1	1	2	3	4	5	6	7	8	9	10
2	2	4	6	8	10	12	14	16	18	20
3	3	6	9	12	15	18	21	24	27	30
4	4	8	12	16	20	24	28	32	36	40
5	5	10	15	20	25	30	35	40	45	50
6	6	12	18	24	30	36	42	48	54	60
7	7	14	21	28	35	42	49	56	63	70
8	8	16	24	32	40	48	56	64	72	80
9	9	18	27	36	45	54	63	72	81	90
10	10	20	30	40	50	60	70	80	90	100

On the multiplication table labeled Doubles, look for rows that have products that are double the products in other rows.

7 Name the factors that have products that are double the products of another factor.

_____

_____

_____

_____

Doubles

×	1	2	3	4	5	6	7	8	9	10
1	1	2	3	4	5	6	7	8	9	10
2	2	4	6	8	10	12	14	16	18	20
3	3	6	9	12	15	18	21	24	27	30
4	4	8	12	16	20	24	28	32	36	40
5	5	10	15	20	25	30	35	40	45	50
6	6	12	18	24	30	36	42	48	54	60
7	7	14	21	28	35	42	49	56	63	70
8	8	16	24	32	40	48	56	64	72	80
9	9	18	27	36	45	54	63	72	81	90
10	10	20	30	40	50	60	70	80	90	100

8 How can you find 6×9 if you know 3×9? _27_

beacause 3x3=6 and then 6 x 9

Rewrite each list so that the count-by list is correct.

9 3, 6, 9, 12, 16, 18, 21 _3,6,9,12,15,18,21,24,27,30,_

10 7, 14, 21, 27, 35, 42, 49 _7,14,21,28,35,42,49_

Multiplication Patterns

PATH to FLUENCY Explore Square Numbers

Write an equation to show the area of each large square.

⑪ 1 × 1 = 1   ⑫ _____   ⑬ _____   ⑭ _____

 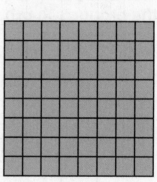

⑮ _____   ⑯ _____

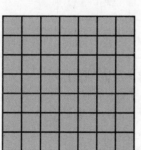 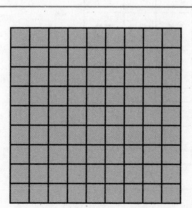 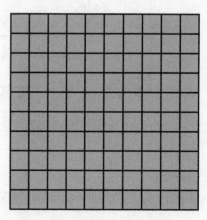

⑰ _____   ⑱ _____

⑲ _____   ⑳ _____

Look for Patterns

21 List the products in Exercises 11–20 in order. Discuss the patterns you see with your class.

_____

The numbers you listed in Exercise 21 are called **square numbers** because they are the areas of squares with whole-number lengths of sides. A square number is the product of a whole number and itself. So, if n is a whole number, the product of $n \times n$ is a square number.

Patterns on the Multiplication Table

22 In the table, circle the products that are square numbers. Discuss the patterns you see with your class.

×	1	2	3	4	5	6	7	8	9	10
1	1	2	3	4	5	6	7	8	9	10
2	2	4	6	8	10	12	14	16	18	20
3	3	6	9	12	15	18	21	24	27	30
4	4	8	12	16	20	24	28	32	36	40
5	5	10	15	20	25	30	35	40	45	50
6	6	12	18	24	30	36	42	48	54	60
7	7	14	21	28	35	42	49	56	63	70
8	8	16	24	32	40	48	56	64	72	80
9	9	18	27	36	45	54	63	72	81	90
10	10	20	30	40	50	60	70	80	90	100

23 Explain why the number 16 is a square number.

_____

Multiplication Patterns

Math Tools: Quick 9s Multiplication

You can use the Quick 9s method to help you multiply by 9. Open your hands and turn them so they are facing you. Imagine that your fingers are numbered like this.

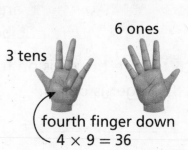

To find a number times 9, bend down the finger for that number. For example, to find 4×9, bend down your fourth finger.

The fingers to the left of your bent finger are the tens. The fingers to the right are the ones. For this problem, there are 3 tens and 6 ones, so $4 \times 9 = 36$.

6 ones

3 tens

fourth finger down
$4 \times 9 = 36$

Why does this work? Because $4 \times 9 = 4 \times (10 - 1) = 40 - 4 = 36$

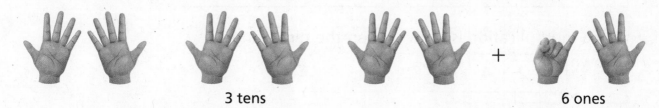

3 tens   +   6 ones

Use Quick 9s to Multiply

24 Write the multiplication that is shown when the seventh multiplier finger is down.

_____ × _____ = _____

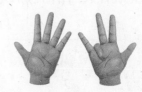

25 Which multiplier finger will be down to show 4 tens and 5 ones?

_____

26 Use Quick 9s to find 8×9.

$8 \times 9 =$ _____

Math Tools: Quick 9s Division

You can also use Quick 9s to help you divide by 9.
For example, to find 72 ÷ 9, show 72 on your fingers.

7 tens   2 ones   Your eighth finger
is down, so 72 ÷ 9 = 8.
$8 \times 9 = 80 - 8 = 72$

27 Write the division that is shown when the fifth multiplier
finger is down.

_____ ÷ _____ = _____

28 Which multiplier finger will be down to show 81 ÷ 9?

_____

29 Which multiplication is shown when the ninth finger
is down?

_____ × _____ = _____

 Check Understanding

Use the picture below. Draw an X on the finger that you would
bend down to find 3 × 9.

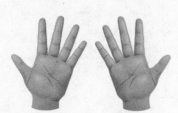

3 × 9 = ☐

Use the picture below. Draw an X on the finger that you would
bend down to find 54 ÷ 9.

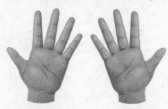

54 ÷ 9 = ☐

Multiplication Patterns

PATH to FLUENCY Play *High Card Wins*

Read the rules for playing *High Card Wins*. Then play the game with your partner.

Rules for *High Card Wins*

Number of players: 2

What you will need: 1 set of Product Cards

1. Shuffle the cards. Deal all the cards evenly between the two players.

2. Players put their stacks in front of them, multiplication side up.

3. Each player takes the top card from his or her stack and puts it multiplication side up in the center of the table.

4. Each player says the product and then turns the card over to check. The correct product is shown in green. Then players do one of the following:

   • If one player says the wrong answer, the other player takes both cards and puts them at the bottom of his or her pile.

   • If both players say the wrong answer, both players take back their cards and put them at the bottom of their piles.

   • If both players say the correct answer, the player with the greater product takes both cards and puts them at the bottom of his or her pile. If the products are the same, the players set the cards aside and play another round. The winner of the next round takes all the cards.

5. Play continues until one player has all the cards.

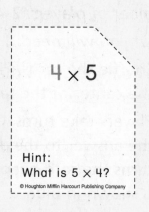

4×5

Hint:
What is 5×4?
© Houghton Mifflin Harcourt Publishing Company

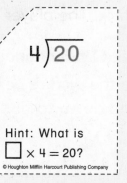

$4 \overline{)20}$

Hint: What is
$\square \times 4 = 20$?
© Houghton Mifflin Harcourt Publishing Company

PATH to FLUENCY Play *Solve the Stack*

Read the rules for playing *Solve the Stack*. Then play the game with your group.

Rules for *Solve the Stack*

Number of players: 2–4

What you will need: 1 set of Product Cards

1. Shuffle the cards. Place them division side up in the center of the table.

2. Players take turns. On each turn, a player says the answer to the division on the top card and then turns the card over to check the answer. The answer is shown in blue.

3. If a player's answer is correct, he or she takes the card. If it is incorrect, the card is placed at the bottom of the stack.

4. Play ends when there are no more cards in the stack. The player with the most cards wins.

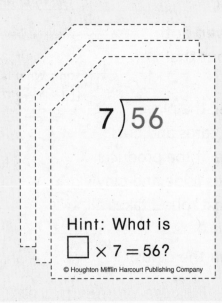

$7\overline{)56}$

Hint: What is
$\square \times 7 = 56$?

© Houghton Mifflin Harcourt Publishing Company

What's My Rule?

Look at the input/output tables below. For every input number, there is only one output number. The rule describes what to do to the input number to get the output number.

Write the rule and then complete each table.

1 **Rule:** X6

Input	Output
7	42
8	48
9	54
6	36
4	24
5	30

2 **Rule:** ÷9

Input	Output
81	9
45	5
72	8
63	7
27	3
54	6

3 **Rule:** ÷3

Input	Output
21	7
27	9
18	6
15	5
24	8
9	3

4 **Rule:** _____

Input	Output
5	25
___	40
9	___
3	15
7	35
___	20

What's My Rule? (continued)

Write the rule and then complete each table.

5 **Rule:** _x2_

Input	Output
2	4
9	18
6	12
4	2
7	14
3	__

40 ÷ 5
5 × __ = 40

6 **Rule:** _x8_

Input	Output
40	5
24	3
16	__
__	4
56	__
__	1

7 **Rule:** _____

Input	Output
50	5
__	8
10	__
__	4
90	__
30	3

8 **Rule:** _____

Input	Output
2	__
7	28
3	12
__	36
__	20
6	__

9 **Rule:** _____

Input	Output
20	4
__	2
35	7
15	__
40	__
__	5

10 **Rule:** _____

Input	Output
7	__
3	21
__	28
6	42
9	__
__	35

 Check Understanding

Explain how you chose the rule for the table in Exercise 9.

Play Multiplication and Division Games

Diagnostic Checkup
for Basic Multiplication

1. $7 \times 5 =$ ___
2. $2 \times 3 =$ ___
3. $9 \times 9 =$ ___
4. $9 \times 6 =$ ___

5. $6 \times 2 =$ ___
6. $3 \times 0 =$ ___
7. $3 \times 4 =$ ___
8. $6 \times 8 =$ ___

9. $5 \times 9 =$ ___
10. $3 \times 3 =$ ___
11. $2 \times 9 =$ ___
12. $5 \times 7 =$ ___

13. $6 \times 10 =$ ___
14. $4 \times 1 =$ ___
15. $6 \times 4 =$ ___
16. $4 \times 8 =$ ___

17. $5 \times 2 =$ ___
18. $1 \times 3 =$ ___
19. $3 \times 9 =$ ___
20. $7 \times 6 =$ ___

21. $7 \times 2 =$ ___
22. $9 \times 0 =$ ___
23. $8 \times 9 =$ ___
24. $8 \times 7 =$ ___

25. $8 \times 10 =$ ___
26. $6 \times 3 =$ ___
27. $4 \times 4 =$ ___
28. $3 \times 8 =$ ___

29. $5 \times 5 =$ ___
30. $6 \times 0 =$ ___
31. $7 \times 9 =$ ___
32. $6 \times 6 =$ ___

33. $9 \times 2 =$ ___
34. $8 \times 3 =$ ___
35. $5 \times 4 =$ ___
36. $7 \times 7 =$ ___

37. $5 \times 10 =$ ___
38. $5 \times 1 =$ ___
39. $10 \times 9 =$ ___
40. $5 \times 6 =$ ___

41. $6 \times 5 =$ ___
42. $9 \times 3 =$ ___
43. $4 \times 2 =$ ___
44. $7 \times 8 =$ ___

45. $8 \times 2 =$ ___
46. $5 \times 0 =$ ___
47. $4 \times 9 =$ ___
48. $6 \times 7 =$ ___

49. $9 \times 5 =$ ___
50. $6 \times 1 =$ ___
51. $7 \times 4 =$ ___
52. $9 \times 8 =$ ___

53. $4 \times 10 =$ ___
54. $5 \times 3 =$ ___
55. $6 \times 9 =$ ___
56. $8 \times 6 =$ ___

57. $8 \times 5 =$ ___
58. $8 \times 0 =$ ___
59. $8 \times 4 =$ ___
60. $4 \times 7 =$ ___

61. $3 \times 5 =$ ___
62. $7 \times 3 =$ ___
63. $5 \times 9 =$ ___
64. $3 \times 6 =$ ___

65. $7 \times 10 =$ ___
66. $8 \times 1 =$ ___
67. $0 \times 4 =$ ___
68. $9 \times 7 =$ ___

Diagnostic Checkup for Basic Division

PATH to FLUENCY

1. $12 \div 2 =$ _____
2. $8 \div 1 =$ _____
3. $36 \div 9 =$ _____
4. $35 \div 7 =$ _____

5. $20 \div 5 =$ _____
6. $24 \div 3 =$ _____
7. $12 \div 4 =$ _____
8. $6 \div 6 =$ _____

9. $6 \div 2 =$ _____
10. $3 \div 3 =$ _____
11. $18 \div 9 =$ _____
12. $63 \div 7 =$ _____

13. $20 \div 10 =$ _____
14. $0 \div 1 =$ _____
15. $40 \div 4 =$ _____
16. $48 \div 8 =$ _____

17. $18 \div 2 =$ _____
18. $6 \div 3 =$ _____
19. $8 \div 4 =$ _____
20. $36 \div 6 =$ _____

21. $8 \div 2 =$ _____
22. $9 \div 1 =$ _____
23. $9 \div 9 =$ _____
24. $56 \div 7 =$ _____

25. $40 \div 5 =$ _____
26. $9 \div 3 =$ _____
27. $36 \div 4 =$ _____
28. $56 \div 8 =$ _____

29. $80 \div 10 =$ _____
30. $7 \div 1 =$ _____
31. $45 \div 9 =$ _____
32. $48 \div 6 =$ _____

33. $5 \div 5 =$ _____
34. $30 \div 3 =$ _____
35. $16 \div 4 =$ _____
36. $72 \div 8 =$ _____

37. $10 \div 2 =$ _____
38. $1 \div 1 =$ _____
39. $54 \div 9 =$ _____
40. $21 \div 7 =$ _____

41. $25 \div 5 =$ _____
42. $15 \div 3 =$ _____
43. $32 \div 4 =$ _____
44. $24 \div 8 =$ _____

45. $90 \div 10 =$ _____
46. $18 \div 3 =$ _____
47. $63 \div 9 =$ _____
48. $54 \div 6 =$ _____

49. $45 \div 5 =$ _____
50. $6 \div 1 =$ _____
51. $20 \div 4 =$ _____
52. $49 \div 7 =$ _____

53. $15 \div 5 =$ _____
54. $0 \div 3 =$ _____
55. $28 \div 4 =$ _____
56. $30 \div 6 =$ _____

57. $16 \div 2 =$ _____
58. $21 \div 3 =$ _____
59. $81 \div 9 =$ _____
60. $64 \div 8 =$ _____

61. $30 \div 5 =$ _____
62. $12 \div 3 =$ _____
63. $27 \div 9 =$ _____
64. $42 \div 7 =$ _____

65. $40 \div 10 =$ _____
66. $10 \div 1 =$ _____
67. $24 \div 4 =$ _____
68. $18 \div 6 =$ _____

Diagnostic Division Checkup

PATH to FLUENCY — Unknown Number Puzzles

Complete each Unknown Number Puzzle.

1

×	6	3	2
10	60	30	20
6	36	18	12
3	18	9	6

2

×	8	4	2
7	56	28	14
2	16	8	4
4	32	16	8

3

×	9	7	
8	72	56	24
6	54	42	18
5	45	35	15

4

×	5	2	8
6	30	12	48
4	20	8	32
9	45	18	72

5

×	5	3	7
6	30	18	42
4	20	12	28
8	40	24	56

6

×	4	9	8
9	36	81	70
3	12	27	24
5	20	45	40

7

×	8	5	7
8	64	40	56
4	32	20	28
3	24	15	21

8

×	3	4	9
9	27	36	81
7	21	28	63
2	6	8	18

9

×	6	2	10
8	48	16	80
7	42	14	70
6	36	12	60

© Houghton Mifflin Harcourt Publishing Company

What's the Error?

Dear Math Students,

Today I had to find 8 × 4. I didn't know the answer, but I figured it out by combining two multiplications I did know:

$$5 \times 2 = 10$$
$$\underline{3 \times 2 = 6}$$
$$8 \times 4 = 16$$

Is my answer right? If not, please correct my work and tell me why it is wrong.

Your friend,
The Puzzled Penguin

10 **Write an answer to Puzzled Penguin.**

_____

_____

_____

Unknown Number Puzzles

11 Make your own Unknown Number Puzzle. Trade with a partner and solve.

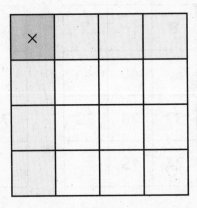

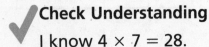 **Check Understanding**

I know 4 × 7 = 28.

So 8 × 7 must be _____ + _____ .

© Houghton Mifflin Harcourt Publishing Company

Check Multiplication and Division Fluency

Write the correct answer.

1 $6 \times 9 = \boxed{}$

2 $18 \div \boxed{} = 2$

3 $8 \times \boxed{} = 56$

4 Write an equation to show the area of the large square.

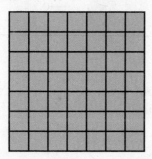

_____

5 Write the rule and complete the table.

Rule:	
Input	**Output**
36	6
30	5
18	_____
54	_____
48	8

Multiply.

1 $1 \times 3 = \boxed{}$

2 $3 \times 2 = \boxed{}$

3 $4 \times 3 = \boxed{}$

4 $4 \times 1 = \boxed{}$

5 $2 \times 5 = \boxed{}$

6 $6 \times 1 = \boxed{}$

7 $6 \times 6 = \boxed{}$

8 $8 \times 4 = \boxed{}$

9 $5 \times 7 = \boxed{}$

10 $9 \times 3 = \boxed{}$

11 $8 \times 8 = \boxed{}$

12 $6 \times 9 = \boxed{}$

13 $7 \times 10 = \boxed{}$

14 $10 \times 10 = \boxed{}$

15 $8 \times 9 = \boxed{}$

Track Blog Traffic

James used a tool to see how much traffic his blog was getting.

Blog Traffic

Month	Unique Users	Number of Unique Users (Rounded)
January	389	400
February	3,725	4,000
March	41,692	40,000

1 James is reporting his blog's growing popularity to a journalist. She asks James how many more unique users visited the blog in February than in January. Should James find the difference using the actual number of unique users or the rounded number of unique users? Explain your answer.

_____

_____

_____

2 On March 3, James's blog was featured in an online gaming journal. How many more unique users visited James's website in March than in February?

_____

3 Look at the *Number of Unique Users (Rounded)* column in the table. Describe a pattern.

_____

4 Is it realistic to expect this pattern to continue? Explain why or why not. Use addition or subtraction patterns to support your answer.

_____

_____

_____

One of the unique users is a computer at a school library. In any given month, anywhere from 250 to 1,200 individual students use this library computer.

5. Consider what you know about the computer in the school's library. Suppose you wanted to include the number of individual students who visited James's blog from that computer. How might the data change?

Complete the table below including your new data.

Blog Traffic

Month	Unique Users + students	Number of Users (Rounded)
January		
February		
March		

6. Explain why you chose the number that you entered for January's data.

_____

_____

_____

7. Explain why you chose the number that you entered for February's data.

_____

_____

_____

8. Explain how you changed the data in March, after James's blog was featured in an online gaming journal.

_____

_____

_____

Dear Family:

In this unit, your child will be learning about the common multiplication method that most adults know. However, they will also explore ways to draw multiplication. *Math Expressions* uses area of rectangles to show multiplication.

	30	+	7
20	$20 \times 30 = 600$		$20 \times 7 = 140$
+			
4	$4 \times 30 = 120$		$4 \times 7 = 28$

Area Method:

$20 \times 30 = 600$
$20 \times 7 = 140$
$4 \times 30 = 120$
$4 \times 7 = 28$
Total $= 888$

Shortcut Method:

$$\begin{array}{r} {}^{1}_{2} \\ 37 \\ \times\ 24 \\ \hline 148 \\ 74 \\ \hline 888 \end{array}$$

Area drawings help all students see multiplication. They also help students remember what numbers they need to multiply and what numbers make up the total.

Your child will also learn to find products involving single-digit numbers, tens, and hundreds by factoring the tens or hundreds. For example,

$$200 \times 30 = 2 \times 100 \times 3 \times 10$$
$$= 2 \times 3 \times 100 \times 10$$
$$= 6 \times 1{,}000 = 6{,}000$$

By observing the zeros patterns in products like these, your child will learn to do such multiplications mentally.

If your child is still not confident with single-digit multiplication and division, we urge you to set aside a few minutes every night for multiplication and division practice. In a few more weeks, the class will be doing multidigit division, so it is very important that your child be both fast and accurate with basic multiplication and division.

If you need practice materials, please contact me.

Sincerely,
Your child's teacher

Estimada familia:

En esta unidad, su niño estará aprendiendo el método de multiplicación común que la mayoría de los adultos conoce. Sin embargo, también explorará maneras de dibujar la multiplicación. Para mostrar la multiplicación, *Math Expressions* usa el método del área del rectángulo.

	30	+	7
20	$20 \times 30 = 600$		$20 \times 7 = 140$
+			
4	$4 \times 30 = 120$		$4 \times 7 = 28$

Método del área

$20 \times 30 = 600$
$20 \times 7 = 140$
$4 \times 30 = 120$
$4 \times 7 = 28$
Total $= 888$

Método más corto

$\overset{1}{\underset{2}{}}$
37
$\times\ 24$
148
74
888

Los dibujos de área ayudan a los estudiantes a visualizar la multiplicación. También los ayuda a recordar cuáles números tienen que multiplicar y cuáles números forman el total.

Su niño también aprenderá a hallar productos relacionados con números de un solo dígito, con decenas y con centenas, factorizando las decenas o las centenas. Por ejemplo:

$200 \times 30 = 2 \times 100 \times 3 \times 10$
$= 2 \times 3 \times 100 \times 10$
$= 6 \times 1,000 = 6,000$

Al observar los patrones de ceros en productos como estos, su niño aprenderá a hacer dichas multiplicaciones mentalmente.

Si su niño todavía no domina la multiplicación y la división con números de un solo dígito, le sugerimos que dedique algunos minutos todas las noches para practicar la multiplicación y la división. Dentro de pocas semanas, la clase hará divisiones con números de varios dígitos, por eso es muy importante que su niño haga las operaciones básicas de multiplicación y de división de manera rápida y exacta.

Si necesita materiales para practicar, comuníquese conmigo.

Atentamente,
El maestro de su niño

Arrays and Area Models

area

estimate

array

partial product

Distributive Property

rounding

A number close to an exact amount or to find about how many or how much.

The number of square units that cover a figure.

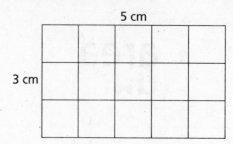

5 cm

3 cm

The product of the ones, or tens, or hundreds, and so on in multidigit multiplication.

Example:

```
   24
 ×  9
 ───
   36  ←  partial product (9 × 4)
  180  ←  partial product (9 × 20)
 ───
  216
```

An arrangement of objects, symbols, or numbers in rows and columns.

Finding the nearest ten, hundred, thousand, or some other place value. The usual rounding rule is to round up if the next digit to the right is 5 or more and round down if the next digit to the right is less than 5.

Example:

463 rounded to the nearest ten is 460.

463 rounded to the nearest hundred is 500.

Multiplying a sum by a number, or multiplying each addend by the number and adding the products; the result is the same.

Example:

$3 \times (2 + 4) = (3 \times 2) + (3 \times 4)$

$3 \times 6 = \quad 6 \quad + \quad 12$

$18 \quad = \quad\quad 18$

square unit
(unit²)

A unit of area equal to
the area of a square with
one-unit sides.

Model a Product of Ones

VOCABULARY
array
area

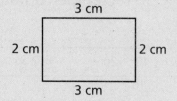

The number of unit squares in an **array** of connected unit squares is the **area** of the rectangle formed by the squares. We sometimes just show the measurement of length and width.

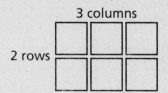
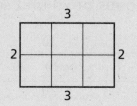

You can draw a rectangle for any multiplication. In the real world, we use multiplication for finding both sizes of arrays and areas of figures.

A 2 × 3 rectangle has 6 unit squares inside, so 2 × 3 = 6.

① On your MathBoard, draw a 3 × 2 rectangle. How is the 3 × 2 rectangle similar to the 2 × 3 rectangle? How is it different?

_____

_____

_____

_____

② How do the areas of the 2 × 3 and 3 × 2 rectangles compare?

_____

_____

_____

Factor the Tens to Multiply Ones and Tens

VOCABULARY
square units

This 2 × 30 rectangle contains 2 groups of 30 unit squares.

```
                    30
 1  ┌──────────────────────────────────┐ 1
 +  │          1 × 30 = 30              │ +
 1  │          1 × 30 = 30              │ 1
    └──────────────────────────────────┘
                    30
```

This 2 × 30 rectangle contains 3 groups of 20 unit squares.

```
   30 =      10         +      10        +      10
    ┌────────────────┬────────────────┬────────────────┐
  2 │   2 × 10 = 20  │   2 × 10 = 20  │   2 × 10 = 20   │ 2
    └────────────────┴────────────────┴────────────────┘
           10        +      10       +      10
```

This 2 × 30 rectangle contains 6 groups of 10 unit squares,
so its area is 60 **square units**.

```
   30 =      10        +      10        +      10
  1 ┌────────────────┬────────────────┬────────────────┐ 1
  1 │  1 × 10 = 10   │  1 × 10 = 10   │  1 × 10 = 10    │ 1
    │  1 × 10 = 10   │  1 × 10 = 10   │  1 × 10 = 10    │
    └────────────────┴────────────────┴────────────────┘
          10        +      10       +      10
```

3 How can we show this numerically? Complete the steps.

$$2 \times 30 = (2 \times 1) \times (\underline{\qquad} \times 10)$$

$$= (\underline{\qquad} \times \underline{\qquad}) \times (1 \times 10)$$

$$= \underline{\qquad} \times 10 = 60$$

4 How is a 30 × 2 rectangle similar to the 2 × 30 rectangle?
How is it different?

_____

_____

_____

_____

✓ Check Understanding

Draw a model to represent 4 × 20. Then show how to
find 4 × 20 by factoring the tens.

Arrays and Area Models

Use Place Value to Multiply

You have learned about the Base Ten Pattern in place value. This model shows how place value and multiplication are connected.

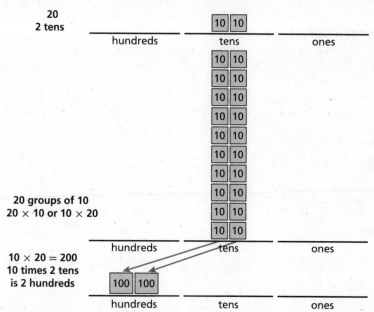

You can use properties to show the relationship between place value and multiplication.

Associative Property $10 \times 20 = 10 \times (2 \times 10)$
                                  $= (10 \times 2) \times 10$

Commutative Property $= (2 \times 10) \times 10$

Associative Property $= 2 \times (10 \times 10)$
                                  $= 2 \times 100$
                                  $= 200$

1 Ten times any number of tens gives you that number of hundreds. Complete the steps to show 10 times 5 tens.

$10 \times 50 = 10 \times ($ _____ $\times$ _____ $)$

$= (10 \times$ _____ $) \times$ _____

$= ($ _____ $\times 10) \times$ _____

$=$ _____ $\times (10 \times$ _____ $)$

$=$ _____ $\times$ _____

$=$ _____

Model a Product of Tens

Olivia wants to tile the top of a table. The table is 20 inches by 30 inches.

2 Find the area of this 20 × 30 rectangle by dividing it into 10-by-10 squares of 100.

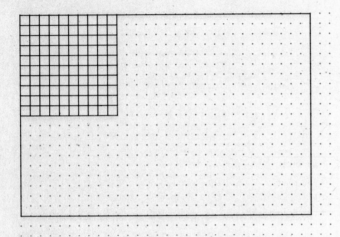

3 Each tile is a 1-inch square. How many tiles does Olivia need to cover the tabletop? _____

4 Each box of tiles contains 100 tiles. How many boxes of tiles does Olivia need to buy? _____

Factor the Tens

5 Show your work in Exercise 2 numerically.

$20 \times 30 = ($ _____ $\times 10) \times ($ _____ $\times 10)$

$= ($ _____ $\times$ _____ $) \times (10 \times 10)$

$=$ _____ $\times 100 = 600$

6 Is it true that 20 × 30 = 30 × 20? Explain how you know.

_____

Check Understanding

Explain how to find 40 × 20 by factoring the tens.

Connect Place Value and Multiplication

Name _____

Look for Patterns

Multiplying greater numbers in your head is easier when you learn patterns of multiplication with tens.

Start with column A and look for the patterns used to get the expressions in each column. Complete the table.

Table 1			
A	**B**	**C**	**D**
2 × 3	2 × 1 × 3 × 1	6 × 1	6
① 2 × 30	2 × 1 × 3 × 10	6 × 10	60
② 20 × 30	2 × 10 × 3 × 10	6 × 100	600

③ How are the expressions in column B different from the expressions in column A?

The expressions are different in column B because in column A they are the multiples of 3 and in column B the multiples are by 10. That is how they are different.

④ In column C, we see that each expression can be written as a number times a place value. Which of these factors gives more information about the size of the product?

_____

_____

⑤ Why is 6 the first digit of the products in column D?

Because it is multiply 3 and 2 so that equals 6.

⑥ Why are there different numbers of zeros in the products in column D?

_____

_____

_____

_____

Compare Tables

Complete each table.

Table 2			
A	B	C	D
6 × 3	6 × 1 × 3 × 1	18 × 1	18
7 6 × 30	6 × 1 × 3 × 10	18 × 10	_____
8 60 × 30	6 × 10 × 3 × 10	_____	_____

Table 3			
A	B	C	D
5 × 8	5 × 1 × 8 × 1	40 × 1	40
9 5 × 80	5 × 1 × 8 × 10	40 × 10	_____
10 50 × 80	_____	_____	_____

11 Why do the products in Table 2 have more digits than the products in Table 1 on page 77?

_____

_____

12 Why are there more zeros in the products in Table 3 than the products in Table 2?

_____

_____

✓ Check Understanding
Complete.

50 × 60 = (_____ × 10) × (6 × _____) = _____ × 100 = _____

Mental Math and Multiplication

Explore the Area Model

20 + 6

4

1 How many square units of area are there in the tens part of the drawing?

_____

2 What multiplication equation gives the area of the tens part of the drawing? Write this equation in its rectangle.

_____

3 How many square units of area are there in the ones part?

_____

4 What multiplication equation gives the area of the ones part? Write this equation in its rectangle.

_____

5 What is the total of the two areas?

_____

6 How do you know that 104 is the correct product of 4×26?

_____

7 Read Problems A and B.

A. Al's photo album has 26 pages. Each page has 4 photos. How many photos are in Al's album?

B. Nick took 4 photos. Henri took 26 photos. How many more photos did Henri take than Nick?

Which problem could you solve using the multiplication you just did? Explain why.

_____

_____

Use Rectangles to Multiply

**Draw a rectangle for each problem on your MathBoard.
Find the tens product, the ones product, and the total.**

8 3×28 **9** 3×29 **10** 5×30 **11** 5×36

_____   _____   _____   _____

_____   _____   _____   _____

_____   _____   _____   _____

12 4×38 **13** 8×38 **14** 4×28 **15** 5×28

_____   _____   _____   _____

_____   _____   _____   _____

_____   _____   _____   _____

Solve each problem.   *Show your work.*

16 Maria's father planted 12 rows of tomatoes in his
garden. Each row had 6 plants. How many tomato
plants were in Maria's father's garden?

_____

17 A library subscribes to 67 magazines. Each month the
library receives 3 copies of each magazine. How many
magazines does the library receive each month?

_____

18 Complete this word problem. Then solve it.

_____ has _____ boxes of _____.

There are _____ _____ in each box.

How many _____ does _____

have altogether? _____

Model One-Digit by Two-Digit Multiplication

Name Sidra Saeed

Multiply One-Digit Dollar Amounts by Two-Digit Numbers

You can use your skills for multiplying a one-digit number by a two-digit number to multiply one-digit dollar amounts by two-digit numbers.

Find the exact cost. Give your answer in dollars.

Show your work.

19 A small package of construction paper costs $2. If someone is purchasing 24 packages, how much will it cost?

It will cost $48 ✓

20 ──── 4
$2 | 40 | 8

20 A box lunch can be purchased for $3. How much will 83 lunches cost?

They will cost $249

80 ──── 3
$3 | 240 | 9

21 A movie ticket costs $8 per person. If 61 people go to the 10:00 A.M. show, how much money does the theater collect for that show?

$47

6,12,18,24,
29,35,41,47

60 + 1
$8 | |

⊢⊢⊢⊢⊢⊢⊢⊢

22 A round-trip train ticket costs $4 per child. If 58 fourth graders take a class trip to the city on the train, how much will the train tickets cost altogether?

$ 232

50   8
$4 | 200 |

23 Admission to the planetarium costs $8 per student. If a group of 72 students takes a trip to the planetarium, how much will their tickets cost altogether?

560+16=576 $576

70   2
8 | 560 | 16

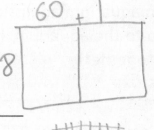

    560
  + 16
    576

24 Sara earns $9 per hour as a cashier. How much does she earn in a 40-hour week?

$360

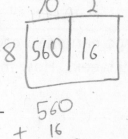

40   0
9 | 360 | 0

Model One-Digit by Two-Digit Multiplication **83**

Multiply Two-Digit Dollar Amounts by One-Digit Numbers

You can use your skills for multiplying a one-digit number by a two-digit number to multiply one-digit numbers by two-digit dollar amounts.

Find the exact cost. Give your answer in dollars.

Show your work.

25 A tricycle costs $53. If 2 tricycles are purchased, how much will the total cost be?

$106   50 3
            2⟌10 6

26 A store sells used video games for $14 each. If someone buys 7 of them, how much will they cost altogether?

7+28=35 it will cost 35$ 7⟌7 8

27 An aquarium admission fee is $23 per person. If 4 friends go to the aquarium, how much will their tickets cost altogether?

80+12=92 92$ 80 12
                   4⟌80 12

28 A car rental costs $72 per day. How much will it cost to rent a car for 3 days?

216   210 6
              3⟌210 6

29 A bus ticket costs $87. How much will 6 tickets cost?

480+42=522   80 7
                6⟌480 42

30 Jorge earns $99 each week. He goes on vacation in 9 weeks. How much will he earn before his vacation?

810+81=891   90 9
                9⟌810 81

✔ **Check Understanding**

Draw an area model to represent Problem 28. Then explain how to use the model to find the product.

© Houghton Mifflin Harcourt Publishing Company

Model One-Digit by Two-Digit Multiplication

Name _Sirlua_

Estimate Products

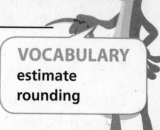

VOCABULARY
estimate
rounding

It is easier to **estimate** the product of a two-digit number and a one-digit number when you think about the two multiples of ten close to the two-digit number. This is shown in the drawings below.

1. In each drawing, find the rectangles that represent 4 × 70 and 4 × 60. These rectangles "frame" the rectangles for 4 × 68 and 4 × 63. Find the values of 4 × 70 and 4 × 60.

   4 × 70 = __280__   4 × 60 = __240__

2. Look at the rectangle that represents 4 × 68. Is 4 × 68 closer to 4 × 60 or to 4 × 70? So is 4 × 68 closer to 240 or 280?

   Its closer to 4×70=280

3. Look at the rectangle that represents 4 × 63. Is 4 × 63 closer to 4 × 60 or to 4 × 70? Is 4 × 63 closer to 240 or 280?

   Its closer to 4×60=240

4. Explain how to use **rounding** to estimate the product of a one-digit number and a two-digit number.

   _____

   _____

   _____

Practice Estimation

Explain how rounding and estimation could help solve these problems.

5 Keesha's school has 185 fourth-grade students. The library has 28 tables with 6 chairs at each table. Can all of the fourth graders sit in the library at one time? How do you know?

_____

_____

_____

_____

6 Ameena is printing the class newsletter. There are 8 pages in the newsletter, and she needs 74 copies. Each package of paper contains 90 sheets. How many packages of paper does she need to print the newsletter?

_____

_____

_____

_____

Estimate each product. Then solve to check your estimate.

7 3×52 _____

8 7×48 _____

9 9×27 _____

10 8×34 _____

✓ **Check Understanding**

Explain how you can use rounding to estimate 3×57.

Estimate Products

Name _____

Use the Place Value Sections Method

You can use an area model to demonstrate the Place Value Sections Method. This strategy is used below for multiplying a one-digit number by a two-digit number.

Complete the steps.

27 =	20	+	7	
5	$5 \times 20 = 100$		$5 \times 7 = 35$	

$5 \quad \begin{array}{r} \underline{} \\ + \\ \hline \underline{} \end{array}$

Use the Place Value Sections Method to solve the problem. Complete the steps.

1 The fourth-grade class is participating in a walk-a-thon. Each student will walk 8 laps around the track. There are 92 fourth-grade students. How many laps will the fourth-grade class walk?

_____

92 =	90	+	2	
8	___ × ___ = ___		___ × ___ = ___	

$8 \quad \begin{array}{r} \underline{} \\ + \\ \hline \underline{} \end{array}$

Draw an area model and use the Place Value Sections Method to solve the problem.

2 A football coach is ordering 3 shirts for each football player. There are 54 players in the football program. How many shirts does the coach need to order for the entire program?

_____

Use the Expanded Notation Method

You can also use an area model to show how to use the Expanded Notation Method.

Use the Expanded Notation Method to solve each problem.

3

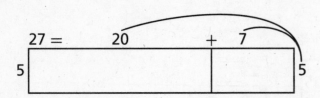

27 = _____ + _____
× 5 =   _____
_____ × _____ = _____
_____ × _____ = _____
                    _____

4 A farm stand sold 4 bushels of apples in one day. Each bushel of apples weighs 42 pounds. How many pounds of apples did the farm stand sell?

_____

_____ = _____ + _____
_____ =
_____ × _____ = _____
_____ × _____ = _____
                    _____

5 A marina needs to replace the boards on their pier. The pier is 7 feet by 39 feet. What is the area of the pier?

_____

Check Understanding

Do you prefer to use the Place Value Sections Method or the Expanded Notation Method? Explain your answer.

Use Place Value to Multiply

Model the Distributive Property

VOCABULARY
Distributive Property
partial product

You have used area models to help you multiply. You can use the area model to find 3 × 74 by writing 74 in expanded form and using the **Distributive Property** to find **partial products**. After you find all the partial products, you can add them together to find the actual product of 3 × 74.

Complete each exercise.

1 Write 74 in expanded form.

3 × 74 = 3 (_____ + _____)

2 Use the Distributive Property.

3 × 74 = (_____ × _____) + (_____ × _____)

The area models below show the steps to find the solution to 3 × 74.

STEP 1   74 =

| 70 | + 4 |

3 | 3 × 70 = 210 | | 3

Multiply the tens.

(3 × 70) = _____

STEP 2   74 =

| 70 | + 4 |

3 | | 3 × 4 = 12 | 3

Multiply the ones.

(3 × 4) = _____

STEP 3   74 =

| 70 | + 4 |

3 | 3 × 70 = 210 | 3 × 4 = 12 | 3

Add the partial products.

```
  210
+  12
_____
```

3 What is the actual product of 3 × 74? _____

Use the Algebraic Notation Method to Multiply

Another numerical multiplication method that can be represented by an area model is the Algebraic Notation Method. This method also decomposes the two-digit factor into tens and ones and then uses the Distributive Property.

Use the Algebraic Notation Method to solve each problem. Complete the steps.

4 8 · 62

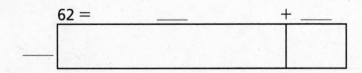

8 · 62 = ____ · (____ + ____)
   = 480 + 16
   = 496

5 2 · 97

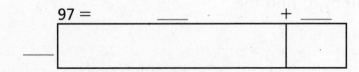

2 · 97 = ____ · (____ + ____)
   = 180 + 14
   = 194

Draw an area model and use the Algebraic Notation Method to solve the problem.

6 There are 9 members on the school's golf team. Each golfer hit a bucket of 68 golf balls at the driving range. How many golf balls did the entire team hit?

_____

✓ Check Understanding

Draw an area model and use it to explain how to use the Algebraic Notation Method to find 4 × 86.

Algebraic Notation Method

Numerical Multiplication Methods

You have used the area model to help you multiply. In
this lesson, you will compare the numerical multiplication
methods that are related to this area model.

Place Value Sections Method

37 =   30   +   7

| 4 | $4 \times 30 = 120$ | $4 \times 7 = 28$ | 4 |

$$\begin{array}{r} 120 \\ +\ 28 \\ \hline 148 \end{array}$$

Expanded Notation Method

37 =   30   +   7

| 4 | | 4 |

$$37 = 30 + 7$$
$$\times\ 4 = \qquad 4$$
$$\overline{4 \times 30 = 120}$$
$$\underline{4 \times\ 7 =\ \ 28}$$
$$\qquad\qquad 148$$

Algebraic Notation Method

37 =   30   +   7

| 4 | | |

$$4 \times 37 = 4 \times (30 + 7)$$
$$= 120 + 28$$
$$= 148$$

Connect the Multiplication Methods

Refer to the examples above.

1 What two values are added together to give the answer
in all three methods?

_____

2 What is different about the three methods?

_____

Practice Different Methods

Fill in the blanks in the following solutions.

3 4 × 86

Expanded Notation

$$86 = \underline{\quad} + 6$$

$$\underline{\times\ \ 4} = \underline{\qquad}\ \ \underline{\quad}$$

$$4 \times \underline{\quad} = \underline{\quad}$$

$$\underline{\quad} \times 6 = 24$$

$$\underline{\qquad}$$

Algebraic Notation

$$4 \cdot 86 = \underline{\quad} \cdot (80 + 6)$$

$$= 320 + \underline{\quad}$$

$$= \underline{\quad}$$

4 4 × 68

Expanded Notation

$$\underline{\quad} = 60 + 8$$

$$\underline{\times\ \ 4} = \underline{\quad}$$

$$4 \times \underline{\quad} = \underline{\quad}$$

$$\underline{\quad} \times 8 = 32$$

$$\underline{\quad}$$

Algebraic Notation

$$4 \cdot 68 = 4 \cdot (\underline{\quad} + \underline{\quad})$$

$$= 240 + \underline{\quad}$$

$$= \underline{\quad}$$

Solve using a numerical method. Draw the related area model.

5 5 × 64 = _____

6 6 × 72 = _____

✓ Check Understanding

For Exercise 6, which numerical method did you use?

_____

Explain why you chose that method.

Compare Methods of One-Digit by Two-Digit Multiplication

Compare Multiplication Methods

Compare these methods for solving 9 × 28.

Method A	Method B	Method C	Method D
$28 = 20 + 8$	$28 = 20 + 8$	28	28
$\times\ 9 = \qquad 9$	$\times\ 9 = \qquad 9$	$\times\ \ 9$	$\times\ \ 9$
$9 \times 20 = 180$	180	180	72
$9 \times 8 =\ \ 72$	72	72	180
252	252	252	252

1 How are all the methods similar? List at least two similarities.

_____

_____

_____

2 How are the methods different? List at least three differences.

_____

_____

_____

_____

Discuss how the recording methods below show the partial products in different ways.

Show Partial Products Method		Show New Groups Method
28		28
$\times\ \ 9$		$\times\ \ 9$
72	9×8	$^{1\ 7}$
$+\ 180$	9×2 tens	$\underline{\ \ \ 82}$
		252

Discuss the Shortcut Method

The steps for the Shortcut Method are shown below.

Shortcut Method with New Groups Above		
Method E:	**Step 1**	**Step 2**
	$\overset{7}{28}$	$\overset{7}{28}$
	$\times\ 9$	$\times\ 9$
	$\overline{2}$	$\overline{252}$

Shortcut Method with New Groups Below		
Method F:	**Step 1**	**Step 2**
	28	28
	$\times\ 9$	$\times\ 9$
	$\overline{{}^{7}2}$	$\overline{\overset{7}{252}}$

3 Where are the products 180 and 72 from Methods A–D?

_____

_____

_____

_____

Practice Multiplication

Solve using any method. Sketch a rectangle if necessary.

4 $\begin{array}{r} 63 \\ \times\ 5 \\ \hline \end{array}$ **5** $\begin{array}{r} 39 \\ \times\ 8 \\ \hline \end{array}$ **6** $\begin{array}{r} 98 \\ \times\ 2 \\ \hline \end{array}$ **7** $\begin{array}{r} 86 \\ \times\ 4 \\ \hline \end{array}$

8 $\begin{array}{r} 25 \\ \times\ 7 \\ \hline \end{array}$ **9** $\begin{array}{r} 47 \\ \times\ 9 \\ \hline \end{array}$ **10** $\begin{array}{r} 76 \\ \times\ 3 \\ \hline \end{array}$ **11** $\begin{array}{r} 54 \\ \times\ 6 \\ \hline \end{array}$

✓ **Check Understanding**

Choose any method shown in this lesson. Explain step-by-step how to use that method to solve 4×37.

Discuss Different Methods

Use Rectangles to Multiply Hundreds

You can use a model to show multiplication with hundreds.
Study this model to see how we can multiply 7 × 300.

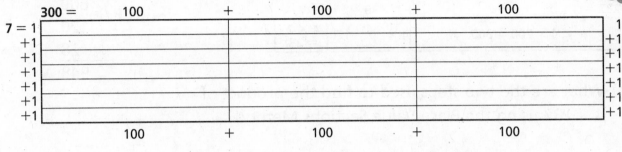

$$7 \times 300 = 7 \times (3 \times 100) = (7 \times 3) \times 100$$

$$= 21 \times 100$$

$$= 2,100$$

1 How many hundreds are represented in each column of the model?

_____

2 How does knowing that 7 × 3 = 21 help you find 7 × 300?

_____

_____

3 What property of multiplication is used in the equation, 7 × (3 × 100) = (7 × 3) × 100?

_____

4 Sketch a model of 6 × 400. Be ready to explain your model.

Compare the Three Methods

You can use the **Place Value Sections Method** to multiply a one-digit number by a three-digit number.

237 =	200	+	30	+	7	
4	4 × 200 = 800		4 × 30 = 120	4 × 7 = 28		4

$$
\begin{aligned}
800 \\
120 \\
+\ 28 \\
\hline
948
\end{aligned}
$$

5 What are the two steps used to find the product of 4 × 237 using the Place Value Sections Method?

_____

The **Expanded Notation Method** uses the same steps as the Place Value Sections Method.

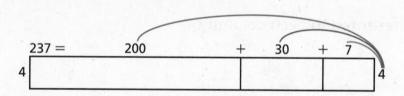

$$
\begin{aligned}
237 &= 200 + 30 + 7 \\
\times\ 4 &= \qquad\qquad\quad 4 \\
\hline
4 \times 200 &= 800 \\
4 \times 30 &= 120 \\
4 \times 7 &=\ \ 28 \\
\hline
&\ \ 948
\end{aligned}
$$

6 What is the last step in the Expanded Notation Method and the Place Value Sections Method?

_____

The **Algebraic Notation Method** uses expanded form just like the other two methods. Even though the steps look different, they are the same as in the other methods.

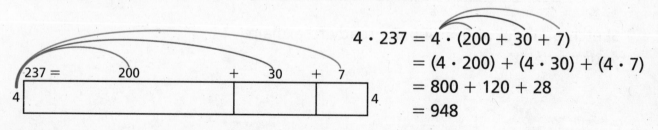

$$
\begin{aligned}
4 \cdot 237 &= 4 \cdot (200 + 30 + 7) \\
&= (4 \cdot 200) + (4 \cdot 30) + (4 \cdot 7) \\
&= 800 + 120 + 28 \\
&= 948
\end{aligned}
$$

7 What is the first step in all three methods?

_____

One-Digit by Three-Digit Multiplication

Name _____

Practice Multiplication

Solve using any method. Show your work.
Draw an area model if necessary.

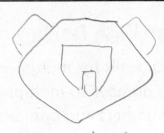

8 $7 \times 321 =$ __2247__

	300	20	1
7	2100	140	7

$(7 \times 300) + 7 \times 20) + (7 \times 1)$ ✓

9 $5 \times 218 =$ __1,090__

	200	10	8
5	1,000	50	40

```
   1,000
      50
      40
   ─────
   1,090
```
✓

$(5 \times 200) + 5 \times 10) + (5 \times 8)$

10 $612 \times 2 =$ __1224__

```
    612
  ×   2
  ─────
  1,224
```
✓

$(2 \times 600) + (2 \times 10) + 2 \times 2)$

11 $154 \times 6 =$ __924__

```
     2
   154
  ×  6
  ────
   924
```

$(6 \times 100) + 6 \times 50) (6 \times 4)$

12 $236 \times 4 =$ __264__

```
    2
  236
  ×  4
  ─────
  = 864
```

$(4 \times 200) + (4 \times 30) + 4 \times 6)$

13 $3 \times 273 =$ __1219__

```
     2
   273
  ×  3
  ─────
   1219
```

$(3 \times 200) + (3 \times 70) + (3 \times 3)$

14 $482 \times 9 =$ _____

```
  482
    9
  ─────
```

15 $8 \times 615 =$ _____

Multiplication With Dollar Amounts

You can use your skills for multiplying a one-digit number by a three-digit number to multiply one-digit dollar amounts by three-digit numbers and one-digit numbers by three-digit dollar amounts.

Find the exact cost. Give your answer in dollars.

Show your work.

16 A car tire costs $158. If Danica needs to buy new tires, how much will 4 tires cost?

_____

17 The fourth grade is going on a field trip to a wildlife sanctuary. A ticket costs $6. How much will it cost if 127 students go on the field trip?

_____

18 A round-trip airplane ticket costs $224. If a group of 5 people buy tickets, how much will their tickets cost?

_____

19 A bookstore orders 325 copies of a book at $7 each. How much does the store pay for the books?

_____

20 During the summer, Joe makes $115 each week mowing lawns. How much will Joe make in 9 weeks?

_____

21 A ticket to the school talent show costs $8. There are 540 seats. If all the seats are filled, how much money does the school collect for that show?

_____

✓ **Check Understanding**

Find the product of a 3-digit number and a 1-digit number using any method. Explain your method.

One-Digit by Three-Digit Multiplication

Discuss Problems With Too Much Information

A word problem may sometimes include more information than you need. Read the following problem and then answer each question.

Mrs. Sanchez is putting a border around her garden. Her garden is a rectangle with dimensions 12 feet by 18 feet. The border material costs $3.00 per foot. How many feet of border material is needed?

1 Identify any extra numerical information. Why isn't this information needed?

$3.00 per foot is the extra numerical information

60 - f'

2 Solve the problem. $P = s + s + s + s + (2 \times 12) + (2 \times 18)$

24 + 36 = 60 ft

Solve each problem. Cross out information that is not needed.

Show your work.

3 Judy downloaded an album for $15. The album has 13 songs. Each song is 3 minutes long. How long will it take to listen to the whole album?

39 mins

$$\begin{array}{r} 13 \\ \times\ 3 \\ \hline 39 \end{array}$$

4 Jerry has 64 coins in his coin collection and 22 stamps in his stamp collection. His sister has 59 stamps in her collection. How many stamps do they have altogether?

81 stamps together

$$\begin{array}{r} 59 \\ +22 \\ \hline = 81 \end{array}$$

5 Adrian has been playing the piano for 3 years. He practices 20 minutes a day. He is preparing for a recital that is 9 days away. How many minutes of practice will he complete before the recital?

180 mins

$$\begin{array}{r} 20 \\ \times\ 9 \\ \hline 189 \end{array}$$

Discuss Problems With Too Little Information

When solving problems in real life, you need to determine what information is needed to solve the problem. Read the following problem and then answer each question.

The campers and staff of a day camp are going to an amusement park on a bus. Each bus holds 26 people. How many buses will be needed?

6 Do you have enough information to solve this problem? What additional information do you need?

No, Because it dosen't tell how many kids are in the bus.

Determine if the problem can be solved. If it cannot be solved, tell what information is missing. If it can be solved, solve it.

7 Richard is saving $5 a week to buy a bike. When will he have enough money?

I dont know how much the bike is.

8 Natalie wants to find out how much her cat weighs. She picks him up and steps on the scale. Together, they weigh 94 pounds. How much does the cat weigh?

I dont know how much the girl wa weighs.

9 Phyllis wants to make 8 potholders. She needs 36 loops for each potholder. How many loops does she need?

Phyllis will need 288 loops.

$$\begin{array}{r} 36 \\ \times\ 8 \\ \hline = 288 \end{array}$$

10 For one of the problems that could not be solved, rewrite it so it can be solved and then solve it.

Richard is saving $5 dollers a week to get his bike. The bike is $12 dollars. When will Richard has enogh.

Multistep Word Problems

Name Sidra Saeed Monatha

Discuss Problems With Hidden Questions

Mrs. Norton bought 2 packages of white cheese with 8 slices in each pack. She bought 3 packages of yellow cheese with 16 slices in each pack. How many more slices of yellow cheese than white cheese did she buy?

11 What do you need to find?

How much more yellow she boght
wure comaring yellow + white

12 What are the hidden questions?

How much white cheese
How much yellow cheese

13 Answer the hidden questions to solve the problem.

How many slices of white cheese? $2 \times 8 =$ ___16___

How many slices of yellow cheese? $3 \times 16 =$ ___48___

How many more slices of yellow cheese? $48 - 16 =$ ___32___

Read the problem. Then answer the questions.

Show your work.

Maurice has 6 boxes of markers. June has 5 boxes of markers. Each box contains 8 markers. How many markers do Maurice and June have altogether?

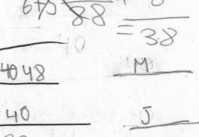

14 Write the hidden questions.

How much does June have and   40 48   M
how much does Maurice have.   + 40   J

15 Solve the problem.

I add 88 markers altogether or
He then multiplied 11 and 8 and go 88

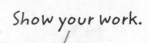

$6 \times 8 = 48$

© Houghton Mifflin Harcourt Publishing Company

Mixed Problem Solving

Show your work.

16 Mr. Collins counts 54 cartons and 5 boxes of paper clips. Each carton contains 8 boxes. A box of paper clips costs $2. How many boxes of paper clips does he have?

_____

17 Ms. Wu has 5 cartons of black ink and 4 cartons of color ink. Each carton contains 48 cartridges. How many ink cartridges are there in all?

_____

What's the Error?

Dear Math Students,

My school is collecting cans for a food drive. There are 608 students in the school. A can of soup costs about $2. Each student will bring in 3 cans. I wrote this multiplication to find the number of cans the school will collect in all.

Is my answer correct? Can you help me?

Your friend,
Puzzled Penguin

$$\begin{array}{r} \overset{2}{608} \\ \times\ \ 3 \\ \hline 1{,}864 \end{array}$$

18 Write a response to Puzzled Penguin.

_____

_____

_____

 Check Understanding

Does Puzzled Penguin's problem have too much information or a hidden question?

_____

Write the information that is extra or the question that is hidden.

_____

Multistep Word Problems

Name _____

Compare Models

A coin-collecting book holds 24 coins on a page. There are
37 pages in the book. How many coins can the book hold?
The models below all show the solution to 24 × 37.

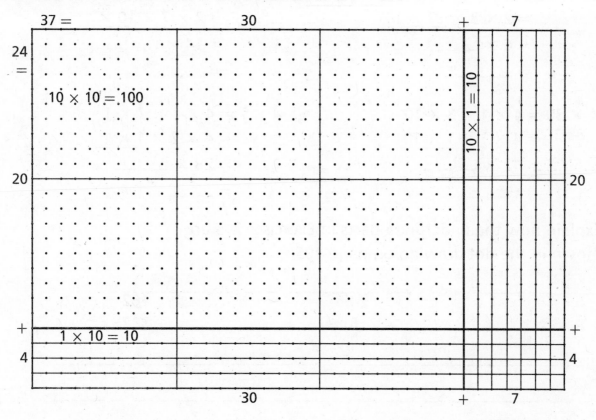

Area Model Sketch

37 =   30   + 7

	30	+ 7
24 = 20	20 × 30 = **600**	20 × 7 = **140**	20
+ 4	4 × 30 = **120**	4 × 7 = **28**	4
	30	+ 7

Place Value Sections Method

$$20 \times 30 = \mathbf{600}$$
$$20 \times 7 = \mathbf{140}$$
$$4 \times 30 = \mathbf{120}$$
$$\underline{4 \times 7 = \mathbf{28}}$$

1. Describe how each model shows 6 hundreds,
   14 tens, 12 tens, and 28 ones.

Investigate Products in the Sketch

Complete each equation.

2 $20 \times 30 = 2 \times 10 \times 3 \times 10$
$= 2 \times 3 \times \underline{10 \times 10}$
$= 6 \times \underline{\hspace{1cm}}$
$= \underline{\hspace{1cm}}$

3 $20 \times 7 = 2 \times 10 \times 7 \times 1$
$= 2 \times 7 \times \underline{10 \times 1}$
$= 14 \times \underline{\hspace{1cm}}$
$= \underline{\hspace{1cm}}$

4 $4 \times 30 = 4 \times 1 \times 3 \times 10$
$= 4 \times 3 \times \underline{1 \times 10}$
$= 12 \times \underline{\hspace{1cm}}$
$= \underline{\hspace{1cm}}$

5 $4 \times 7 = 4 \times 1 \times 7 \times 1$
$= 4 \times 7 \times \underline{1 \times 1}$
$= 28 \times \underline{\hspace{1cm}}$
$= \underline{\hspace{1cm}}$

6 Explain how the underlined parts in Exercises 2–5 are shown in the dot drawing on page 105.

_____

_____

_____

_____

7 Find 24×37 by adding the products in Exercises 2–5.

_____

Practice and Discuss Modeling

Use your MathBoard to sketch an area drawing for each exercise. Then find the product.

8 36×58 _____

9 28×42 _____

10 63×27 _____

11 26×57 _____

12 86×35 _____

13 38×65 _____

✓ **Check Understanding**

Write 4 multiplications you could use to find 25×31.

____ × ____   ____ × ____   ____ × ____   ____ × ____

Two-Digit by Two-Digit Multiplication

Compare Multiplication Methods

Each area model is the same. Study how these three methods of recording 43 × 67 are related to the area models.

Place Value Sections Method

67 =   60   +   7

43 =			
40	40 × 60 = 2,400	40 × 7 = 280	40
+			+
3	3 × 60 = 180	3 × 7 = 21	3
	60	+	7

$$40 \times 60 = 2,400$$
$$40 \times 7 =280$$
$$3 \times 60 =180$$
$$\underline{3 \times 7 =21}$$
$$2,881$$

Expanded Notation Method

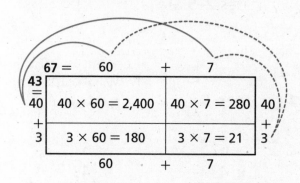

67 =	60	+	7	
43 =				
40	40 × 60 = 2,400	40 × 7 = 280	40
+			+
3	3 × 60 = 180	3 × 7 = 21	3
	60	·	7

$$67 = 60 + 7$$
$$\times\ 43 = 40 + 3$$
$$\overline{}$$
$$40 \times 60 = 2,400$$
$$40 \times 7 =280$$
$$3 \times 60 =180$$
$$\underline{3 \times 7 =21}$$
$$2,881$$

Algebraic Notation Method

67 =	60	+	7	
43 =				
40	40 × 60 = 2,400	40 × 7 = 280	40
3	3 × 60 = 180	3 × 7 = 21	3
	60	+	7

$$43 \cdot 67 = (40 + 3) \cdot (60 + 7)$$
$$= 2,400 + 280 + 180 + 21$$
$$= 2,881$$

1 What is alike about all the three methods?

_____

_____

© Houghton Mifflin Harcourt Publishing Company

Other Ways to Record Multiplication

Discuss how the recording methods below show the partial products in different ways.

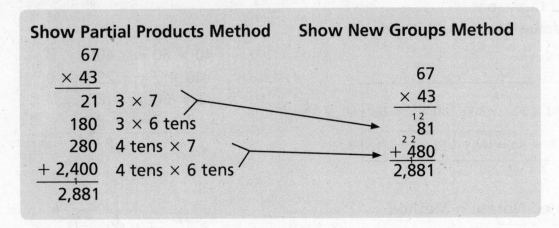

Show Partial Products Method

```
      67
    × 43
      21    3 × 7
     180    3 × 6 tens
     280    4 tens × 7
  + 2,400   4 tens × 6 tens
     1
   2,881
```

Show New Groups Method

```
        67
      × 43
       1 2
        81
       2 2
    + 480
       1
     2,881
```

The Shortcut Method

New Groups Above

Step 1	Step 2	Step 3	Step 4	Step 5

```
  2            2        2 2        2 2        2 2
  67           2        2          2          2
× 43          67       67         67         67
 ─────      × 43     × 43       × 43       × 43
   1        ─────    ─────      ─────      ─────
             201      201        201        201
                        8        268      + 268
                                          ─────
                                          2,881
```

New Groups Below

```
      67
    × 43
     2 2
     201
   + 268
   ─────
    2,881
```

Discuss how this area drawing relates to the Shortcut Method.

	67
40	40 × 67 = 2,680
+	
3	3 × 67 = 201

✓ Check Understanding

Explain how to use any method to multiply 36 × 74.

Different Methods for Two-Digit Multiplication

Estimate Products

Products of two-digit factors can be estimated by rounding each factor to the nearest ten.

Estimate and then solve.

1 28 × 74   **2** 84 × 27   **3** 93 × 57

_____   _____   _____

4 87 × 54   **5** 38 × 62   **6** 65 × 39

_____   _____   _____

7 26 × 43   **8** 59 × 96   **9** 53 × 74

_____   _____   _____

10 Write a multiplication word problem. Estimate the product and then solve.

_____

_____

_____

_____

_____

11 Would using an estimate be problematic in the situation you wrote for Exercise 10? Explain why or why not.

_____

_____

_____

What's the Error?

Dear Math Students,

My friends and I are going to build 42 flower boxes. The building plans say each box needs 13 nails. I rounded to estimate how many nails we'll need. Since $40 \times 10 = 400$, I bought a box of 400 nails.

My friends say we won't have enough nails. Did I make a mistake? Can you help me estimate how many nails we need?

Your friend,
Puzzled Penguin

12 Write a response to Puzzle Penguin.

_____

_____

_____

Estimate and then solve. Explain whether the estimate is problematic in each situation.

13 Sally hires a dog sitter for her 18-day trip. A dog sitter charges $14 per day. How much money will Sally need to pay the dog sitter?

_____

_____

14 An artist draws a plan for a mosaic pattern that has 21 rows of tiles with 47 tiles in each row. How many tiles does the artist need to buy?

_____

_____

_____

✓ **Check Understanding**

Describe strategies you use to estimate products.

Check Products of Two-Digit Numbers

Name _____

Practice Multiplication Methods

1 Multiply 38 × 59.

Shortened Expanded Notation Method   **Shortcut Method**

$$\begin{array}{r} 38 \\ \times\ 59 \\ \hline \end{array}$$

$$\begin{array}{r} 38 \\ \times\ 59 \\ \hline \end{array}$$

Solve using any method and show your work.
Check your work with estimation.

2 43 × 22

_____

3 25 × 25

_____

4 31 × 62

_____

5 54 × 72

_____

6 81 × 33

_____

7 49 × 62

_____

Practice Multiplication

With practice, you will be able to solve a multiplication problem using fewer written steps.

Solve.   *Show your work.*

8 Between his ninth and tenth birthdays, Jimmy read 1 book each week. There are 52 weeks in a year. If each book had about 95 pages, about how many pages did he read during the year?

_____

9 Sam's father built a stone wall in their backyard. The wall was 14 stones high and 79 stones long. How many stones did he use to build the wall?

_____

10 Balloon Bonanza sells party balloons in packages of 25 balloons. There are 48 packages in the store. How many balloons are in 48 packages?

_____

11 Brian is buying T-shirts for the marching band. He knows that at parades the band forms 24 rows. Each row has 13 students. If T-shirts come in boxes of 100, how many boxes of T-shirts should Brian buy?

_____

✓ **Check Understanding**
Find the product of 35×56 using any method.

_____

Multiply using any method. Show your work.

1 48 × 29

2 64 × 37

Estimate and then solve.

3 68 × 97

4 58 × 86

5 Draw an area model for 42 × 56.
Then find the product.

_____

_____

Name _____   **Date** _____

Add or subtract.

1
$$\begin{array}{r} 959,896 \\ -78,929 \\ \hline \end{array}$$

2
$$\begin{array}{r} 361 \\ +728 \\ \hline \end{array}$$

3
$$\begin{array}{r} 196 \\ -154 \\ \hline \end{array}$$

4
$$\begin{array}{r} 7,718 \\ -3,683 \\ \hline \end{array}$$

5
$$\begin{array}{r} 461,727 \\ +88,866 \\ \hline \end{array}$$

6
$$\begin{array}{r} 821 \\ +107 \\ \hline \end{array}$$

7
$$\begin{array}{r} 315,944 \\ -257,061 \\ \hline \end{array}$$

8
$$\begin{array}{r} 71,656 \\ -1,966 \\ \hline \end{array}$$

9
$$\begin{array}{r} 99,181 \\ +1,876 \\ \hline \end{array}$$

10
$$\begin{array}{r} 1,951 \\ -1,311 \\ \hline \end{array}$$

11
$$\begin{array}{r} 815 \\ -673 \\ \hline \end{array}$$

12
$$\begin{array}{r} 22,688 \\ +98,205 \\ \hline \end{array}$$

13
$$\begin{array}{r} 44,827 \\ -28,399 \\ \hline \end{array}$$

14
$$\begin{array}{r} 1,236 \\ +9,535 \\ \hline \end{array}$$

15
$$\begin{array}{r} 8,318 \\ +227 \\ \hline \end{array}$$

Use Rectangles to Multiply Thousands

You can use a model to multiply greater numbers.
Notice that each of the smaller rectangles in this model
represents one thousand. Each of the columns represents
seven one-thousands or 7,000.

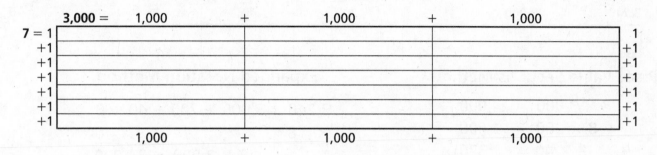

$$7 \times 3{,}000 = 7 \times (3 \times 1{,}000) = (7 \times 3) \times 1{,}000$$
$$= 21 \times 1{,}000$$
$$= 21{,}000$$

1 While multiplying by thousands, how many zeros can
you expect in the product?

_____

2 How does thinking of 3,000 as 3 × 1,000 help you to
multiply 7 × 3,000?

_____

_____

_____

3 Draw a model for 4 × 8,000. Then find the product.

_____

Compare Multiplication Methods

You can use the multiplication methods you have learned to multiply a one-digit number by a four-digit number.

Find 8 × 3,248.

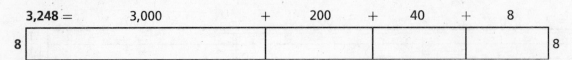

3,248 =	3,000	+	200	+	40	+	8	

Place Value Sections Method

$$8 \times 3,000 = 24,000$$
$$8 \times 200 = 1,600$$
$$8 \times 40 = 320$$
$$8 \times 8 = 64$$
$$\overline{25,984}$$

Expanded Notation Method

$$3,248 = 3,000 + 200 + 40 + 8$$
$$\times \quad 8 = 8$$
$$8 \times 3,000 = 24,000$$
$$8 \times 200 = 1,600$$
$$8 \times 40 = 320$$
$$8 \times 8 = 64$$
$$\overline{25,984}$$

Algebraic Notation Method

$$8 \times 3,248 = 8 \times (3,000 + 200 + 40 + 8)$$
$$= (8 \times 3,000) + (8 \times 200) + (8 \times 40) + (8 \times 8)$$
$$= 24,000 + 1,600 + 320 + 64$$
$$= 25,984$$

Make a rectangle drawing for each problem on your MathBoard. Then solve the problem using the method of your choice.

④ $3 \times 8,153 = $ _____

⑤ $4 \times 2,961 = $ _____

⑥ $6 \times 5,287 = $ _____

⑦ $7 \times 1,733 = $ _____

✓ **Check Understanding**

Draw a model for $9 \times 5,432$. Then find the product using the method of your choice.

© Houghton Mifflin Harcourt Publishing Company

Multiply One-Digit and Four-Digit Numbers

Compare Methods of Multiplication

Look at the drawing and the six numerical solutions for 4 × 2,237.

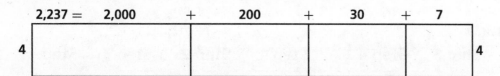

	Method A	Method B	Method C	Method D	Method E	Method F
	2,237 = 2,000 + 200 + 30 + 7	2,237 = 2,000 + 200 + 30 + 7	2,237	2,237	$\overset{1\,2}{2,237}$	2,237
	× 4 = 4	× 4 = 4	× 4	× 4	× 4	× 4
	4 × 2,000 = 8,000	8,000	8,000	28	8,948	$\overline{\overset{1\,2}{8,948}}$
	4 × 200 = 800	800	800	120		
	4 × 30 = 120	120	120	800		
	4 × 7 = 28	28	28	8,000		
	8,948	8,948	8,948	8,948		

1 How are the solutions similar? List at least two ways.

_____

_____

_____

2 How are the solutions different? List at least three comparisons between methods.

_____

_____

_____

_____

_____

3 How do Methods A–D relate to the drawing? List at least two ways.

_____

_____

_____

Analyze the Shortcut Method

Look at this breakdown of solution steps for Method E and Method F.

	Method E		
Step 1	**Step 2**	**Step 3**	**Step 4**
$\overset{2}{2{,}237}$	$\overset{1\,2}{2{,}237}$	$\overset{1\,2}{2{,}237}$	$\overset{1\,2}{2{,}237}$
$\times\quad 4$	$\times\quad 4$	$\times\quad 4$	$\times\quad 4$
8	48	948	$8{,}948$

	Method F		
Step 1	**Step 2**	**Step 3**	**Step 4**
$2{,}237$	$2{,}237$	$2{,}237$	$2{,}237$
$\times\ _{2}4$	$\times\ _{1\,2}4$	$\times\ _{1\,2}4$	$\times\ _{1\,2}4$
8	48	948	$8{,}948$

4 Describe what happens in Step 1.

_____

_____

_____

5 Describe what happens in Step 2.

_____

_____

_____

_____

6 Describe what happens in Step 3.

_____

_____

_____

_____

7 Describe what happens in Step 4.

_____

_____

_____

Round and Estimate With Thousands and Hundreds

You can use what you know about rounding and multiplication with thousands to estimate the product of $4 \times 3,692$.

8 Find the product if you round up: $4 \times 4,000 =$ _____

9 Find the product if you round down: $4 \times 3,000 =$ _____

10 Which one of the two estimates will be closer to the actual solution? Why?

_____

11 Calculate the actual solution. _____

12 Explain why neither estimate is very close to the actual solution.

_____

_____

13 What would be the estimate if you added 4×600 to $4 \times 3,000$; $(4 \times 3,000) + (4 \times 600)$? _____

14 What would be the estimate if you added 4×700 to $4 \times 3,000$; $(4 \times 3,000) + (4 \times 700)$? _____

15 Estimate $4 \times 7,821$ by rounding 7,821 to the nearest thousand.

_____

16 Find the actual product. _____

17 Find a better estimate for $4 \times 7,821$. Show your work.

_____

_____

Round, estimate, and fix the estimate as needed.

18 $6 \times 3,095$ **19** $7 \times 2,784$

_____   _____

_____   _____

Estimate Products

Solve and then estimate to check if your answer is reasonable. Show your estimate.

20 5 × 3,487 = _____

_____

_____

21 7 × 8,894 = _____

_____

_____

22 4 × 7,812 = _____

_____

_____

23 3 × 4,109 = _____

_____

_____

What's the Error?

Dear Math Students,

My school collected 2,468 empty cartons of milk today. If the school collects about the same number of cartons each day for 5 days, I estimated that the school will collect 17,500 cartons.

$$(5 \times 3,000) + (5 \times 500) = 17,500$$

Can you help me decide if this is a reasonable estimate?

Your friend,
Puzzled Penguin

24 Write a response to Puzzled Penguin.

_____

_____

_____

_____

 Check Understanding

Multiply 6 × 5,283 using the Shortcut Method. _____
Round and estimate to check your work.

_____

Use the Shortcut Method

Practice Mixed Multiplication

Solve using any method and show your work. Check your work with estimation.

1 35 × 9
_____

2 56 × 17
_____

3 228 × 2
_____

4 23
   × 7

5 77
   × 9

6 59
   × 3

7 92
   × 84

8 49
   × 12

9 61
   × 36

10 459
    ×   4

11 588
    ×   6

12 216
    ×   7

13 3,473
    ×   5

14 1,156
    ×   8

15 2,937
    ×   3

Practice With Word Problems

**Solve using any method and show your work.
Check your work with estimation.**

Show your work.

16 A doubles tennis court is 78 feet long and
36 feet wide. A singles tennis court is 78 feet
long and 27 feet wide. What is the difference
between the areas of a doubles tennis court and
a singles tennis court?

_____

17 A movie complex has 8 theaters. Each theater has
287 seats. There are 13 people who work at the theater.
How many seats are there altogether?

_____

18 Jenny goes to a 55-minute-long dance class 3 days each
week. There are 9 weeks until the class recital. How
many minutes of dance class are there until the recital?

_____

19 Alex is shopping for school clothes. He buys 4 shirts
for $12 each. He also buys 3 pairs of shorts for $17
each. How much does Alex spend on school clothes
in all?

_____

20 Casey draws a rectangular array that is 1,167 units
long and 7 units wide. What is the area of
Casey's array?

_____

✓ **Check Understanding**
Multiply 4 × 6,689 using any method. _____
Check your work with estimation.

Practice Multiplying

Math and Games

This is a game called *Big City Building*. The goal of the game is to design and build a successful city within a budget. To win the game, the city must have all of the features of a real-life city such as apartments, schools, parks, and shops, so its residents will be happy.

1 Each city in *Big City Building* requires a fire station, a police station, and a post office. These each cost $2,657 in taxes per year to maintain. How much does it cost to maintain the fire station, the police station, and the post office building for one year?

_____

2 In *Big City Building*, the roads are standard two-lane roads. The total width of the road is 9 meters. If each block is 82 meters long, what is the area of the road of one city block in square meters?

Big City Building

The table shows the cost of different features on the *Big City Building* game. Below is Scott's design, so far, for his city in *Big City Building*.

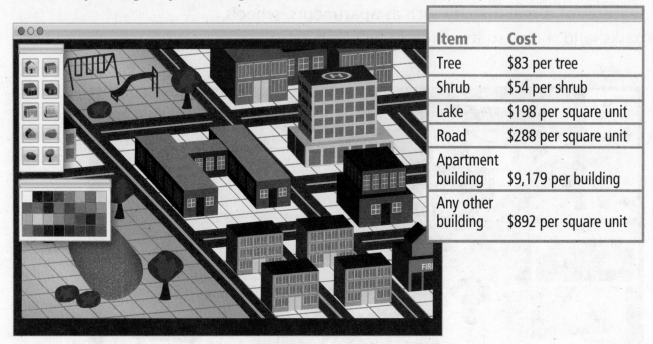

Item	Cost
Tree	$83 per tree
Shrub	$54 per shrub
Lake	$198 per square unit
Road	$288 per square unit
Apartment building	$9,179 per building
Any other building	$892 per square unit

Currently, Scott has $156,324 in *Big City Building* money to create his city.

3 Scott buys 42 trees to put in the park. The trees cost $83 each. How much money does Scott pay for the trees?

_____

4 Each apartment building contains 59 apartment units. Scott has 4 apartment buildings in his city. How many apartment units does Scott's city have?

_____

5 If Scott's city is 27 units long and 19 units wide, what is the area of Scott's city in square units?

_____

Focus on Problem Solving

Multiply using any method. Show your work.

1 $4 \times 3,819$

2 $6,423 \times 7$

Multiply and then estimate to check if your answer is reasonable.

3 $3 \times 4,756$

4 $6 \times 5,939$

Solve.

Show your work.

5 It costs $9,179 in *Big City Building* game money to build each apartment. What is the cost to build 6 apartment buildings?

Name _____ Date _____

Add or subtract.

1
```
  37,796
+ 68,121
```

2
```
  8,990
+ 8,501
```

3
```
  638
+ 127
```

4
```
  22,274
- 16,139
```

5
```
  20,056
-  4,315
```

6
```
  565
+ 234
```

7
```
  920,443
-  36,071
```

8
```
  118,242
+ 893,915
```

9
```
  324
- 203
```

10
```
  211,549
- 144,096
```

11
```
  4,759
- 3,392
```

12
```
  1,010
+   993
```

13
```
  55,825
+  7,115
```

14
```
  5,898
+ 3,251
```

15
```
  842
- 739
```

1 Use the numbers on the tiles to complete the steps to find
20 × 40 by factoring the tens.

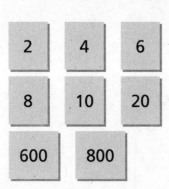

2	4	6
8	10	20
600	800	

$20 \times 40 = (\boxed{} \times 10) \times (\boxed{} \times 10)$

$= (2 \times 4) \times (\boxed{} \times \boxed{})$

$= \boxed{} \times 100$

$= \boxed{}$

2 Select the expression that is equivalent to 36 × 25.
Mark all that apply.

Ⓐ   30 × 6 + 20 × 5

Ⓑ   (30 × 20) + (30 × 5) + (6 × 20) + (6 × 5)

Ⓒ   (5 × 6) + (5 × 3 tens) + (2 tens × 6) + (2 tens × 3 tens)

Ⓓ   30 × (20 + 5) + 6 × (20 + 5)

Ⓔ   30 + 15 + 12 + 6

3 There are 24 pencils in a box. If there are 90 boxes,
how many pencils are there?

_____ pencils

4 A clown bought 18 bags of round balloons with 20 balloons
in each bag. He bought 26 bags of long balloons with
35 balloons in each bag. How many more long balloons
did he buy than round balloons? Show your work.

5 Draw an area model for 7×682.

Explain how you used the model to find the product.

6 For Exercises 6a–6d, choose Yes or No to tell whether the equation is true.

6a. $8 \times 4 = 32$ ○ Yes ○ No

6b. $8 \times 400 = 32,000$ ○ Yes ○ No

6c. $80 \times 40 = 3,200$ ○ Yes ○ No

6d. $8 \times 4,000 = 32,000$ ○ Yes ○ No

7 Find the product of 4×52.

8 Use the numbers on the tiles to complete the
area model for 29 × 48.

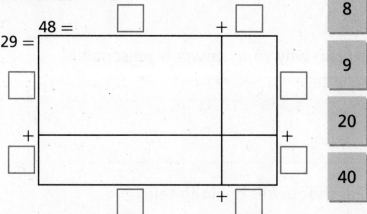

Show how to use the area model and expanded
notation to find 29 × 48.

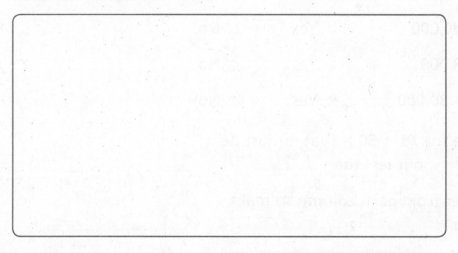

9 Estimate 15 × 34 by rounding each number to the
nearest ten.

10 For Exercises 10a–10d, choose True or False to describe
the statement.

10a. 8 × 93 is greater than 8 × 90.   ○ True   ○ False

10b. An estimate of 8 × 93 is 2,700.   ○ True   ○ False

10c. 8 × 93 = (8 × 9) + (8 × 3)   ○ True   ○ False

10d. 8 × 93 is less than 800.   ○ True   ○ False

Name _____

Date _____

⑪ Find 4 × 7,342.

Use estimation to explain why your answer is reasonable.

```



```

⑫ For Exercises 12a–12d, choose Yes or No to tell
whether the equation is true.

12a. 5 × 60 = 30   ○ Yes   ○ No

12b. 500 × 6 = 30,000   ○ Yes   ○ No

12c. 50 × 60 = 3,000   ○ Yes   ○ No

12d. 5 × 6,000 = 30,000   ○ Yes   ○ No

⑬ The best estimate for 78 × 50 is that it must be
greater than ___?___ but less than ___?___.

Select one number from each column to make
the sentence true.

Greater than	Less than
○ 3,200	○ 3,200
○ 3,500	○ 3,500
○ 4,000	○ 4,000
○ 4,200	○ 4,200

⑭ Choose the number from the box to complete the statement.

The product of 39 and 22 is closest to _____.

```
300

400

800

8,000
```

15 A bus tour of New York City costs $48 per person. A group of 7 people go on the tour. What is the cost for the group? Explain how you found your answer.

16 There is a book sale at the library. The price for each book is $4. If 239 books are sold, how much money will be made at the sale?

Ⓐ $235

Ⓑ $243

Ⓒ $826

Ⓓ $956

17 Volunteers are needed at the animal shelter. If 245 boys and 304 girls each volunteer to work 3 hours, how many volunteer hours is this?

Part A

Identify any extra information given in the problem. Explain your reasoning.

Part B

Solve the problem. Show your work.

18 Select an expression that is equivalent to 7×800.
Mark all that apply.

Ⓐ $8 + (100 \times 7) + 10$ Ⓑ $(8 \times 7) \times (100 \times 1)$

Ⓒ $(7 \times 80) \times 10$ Ⓓ $(8 + 7) \times (100 + 1)$

19 Joe makes belts. He has 9 buckles. He uses 12 rivets on each of 4 belts and 15 rivets on each of 2 belts. He has 22 rivets left over. How many rivets are on the belts?

Part A

Identify any extra information given in the problem.

Part B

Solve the problem. Show your work.

20 Draw an area model for $7 \times 5,432$. Then write an equation to match your model.

Equation: _____ × _____ = _____

21 Use the numbers on the tiles to complete the steps to find the solution to 4×65.

$4 \times 65 = \underline{\hspace{1cm}} \times (60 + \underline{\hspace{1cm}})$

$ = (4 \times \underline{\hspace{1cm}}) + (4 \times \underline{\hspace{1cm}})$

$ = \underline{\hspace{1cm}} + 20$

$ = \underline{\hspace{1cm}}$

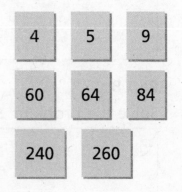

4	5	9
60	64	84
240	260	

Shop for a Clothing Drive

Mrs. Liston and 9 of her friends are
shopping for clothes to donate to a winter
clothing drive. The store has many clothing
items for sale. The table shows the items
Mrs. Liston and her friends can buy and the
price for each item.

Clothing for Sale

Item	Price
Shirt	$15
Jeans	$25
Sweater	$45
Boots	$75
Coat	$99

1 Mrs. Liston has $259. Is it possible for her to spend
the whole amount by buying only one kind of item
at the store? How do you know?

_____

_____

_____

_____

2 What are 2 different ways that Mrs. Liston can
spend $259 at the store?

_____

_____

3 If Mrs. Liston and her friends each spend $259 at the store,
how much money do they spend in all? How do you know?

_____

_____

4 Mrs. Liston collected $1,800 for the clothing drive. She buys
24 pairs of jeans and 24 sweaters. What could she buy with
the money that is left?

_____

_____

_____

_____

The store puts some items on sale, as shown in the table.

Clothing for Sale

Item	Original Price	Sale Price
Shirt	$15	$12
Jeans	$25	
Sweater	$45	$42
Boots	$75	$56
Coat	$99	

5 How would these sale prices affect what Mrs. Liston could have bought with $1,800? Explain.

_____

_____

_____

_____

_____

6 Mrs. Liston and her friends would like to buy a shirt, a pair of jeans, and a sweater for 32 people. They will hold a dinner to raise the money needed to buy these items on sale. They plan to estimate the money needed. Will this help them set an appropriate goal for their dinner? Explain your decision.

_____

_____

_____

_____

7 Explain how to write a word problem that requires multiplication and addition to solve using the information in the table. Give a problem in your explanation.

_____

_____

_____

_____

_____

Dear Family:

Your child is familiar with multiplication from earlier units. Unit 3 of *Math Expressions* extends the concepts used in multiplication to teach your child division. The main goals of this unit are to:

- Learn methods for dividing whole numbers up to four digits by one-digit divisors and up to three digits by two-digit divisors.

- Use estimates to check the reasonableness of answers.

- Solve problems involving division and remainders.

Your child will learn and practice techniques such as the Place Value Sections, Expanded Notation, and Digit-by-Digit methods to gain speed and accuracy in division.

Examples of Division Methods:

Place Value Sections Method	Expanded Notation Method	Digit-by-Digit Method

$$60 + 6 = 66$$

$$
5\begin{array}{|c|c|}
\hline
330 & 30 \\
-300 & 30 \\
\hline
30 & 0 \\
\end{array}
$$

Expanded Notation Method:

$$
\begin{array}{r}
6 \\
60
\end{array} \Big] 66
$$

$$
\begin{array}{r}
5)\overline{330} \\
-300 \\
\hline
30 \\
-30 \\
\hline
0
\end{array}
$$

Digit-by-Digit Method:

$$
\begin{array}{r}
66 \\
5)\overline{330} \\
-30 \\
\hline
30 \\
-30 \\
\hline
0
\end{array}
$$

> Your child may use whatever method he or she chooses as long as he or she can explain it. Some children like to use different methods.

Your child will also learn to interpret remainders in the context of the problem being solved; for example, when the remainder alone is the answer to a word problem.

Your child will apply this knowledge to solve mixed problems with one or more steps and using all four operations.

If you have questions or problems, please contact me.

Sincerely,
Your child's teacher

Estimada familia:

En unidades anteriores su niño se ha familiarizado con la multiplicación. La Unidad 3 de *Math Expressions* amplía los conceptos usados en la multiplicación para que su niño aprenda la división. Los objetivos principales de esta unidad son:

- aprender métodos para dividir números enteros de hasta cuatro dígitos por divisores de un dígito y hasta tres dígitos por divisores de dos dígitos.

- usar la estimación para comprobar si las respuestas son razonables.

- resolver problemas que requieran división y residuos.

Su niño aprenderá y practicará técnicas tales como las de Secciones de valor posicional, Notación extendida y Dígito por dígito, para adquirir rapidez y precisión en la división.

Ejemplos de métodos de división:

Secciones de valor posicional	Notación extendida	Dígito por dígito

$$60 + 6 = 66$$

$$5 \overline{\begin{array}{c|c} 330 & 30 \\ -300 & 30 \\ \hline 30 & 0 \end{array}}$$

$$\left.\begin{array}{r} 6 \\ 60 \end{array}\right] 66$$

$$5\overline{)330}$$
$$\underline{-300}$$
$$30$$
$$\underline{-30}$$
$$0$$

$$66$$
$$5\overline{)330}$$
$$\underline{-30}$$
$$30$$
$$\underline{-30}$$
$$0$$

> Su niño puede usar el método que elija siempre y cuando pueda explicarlo. A algunos niños les gusta usar métodos diferentes.

Su niño también aprenderá a interpretar los residuos en el contexto del problema que se esté resolviendo; por ejemplo, cuando solamente el residuo es la respuesta a un problema.

Su niño aplicará este conocimiento para resolver problemas mixtos de uno o más pasos, usando las cuatro operaciones.

Si tiene alguna pregunta o comentario, por favor comuníquese conmigo.

Atentamente,
El maestro de su niño

Divide with Remainders

compatible
numbers

overestimate

dividend

quotient

divisor

remainder

Make an estimate that is too big.

Numbers that are easy to compute mentally.

Example:

$9\overline{)5,841}$

Some compatible numbers for the divisor and dividend are 9 and 5,400, and 9 and 6,300.

The answer to a division problem.

Example:

$9\overline{)63}$ with 7 above

7 is the quotient.

The number that is divided in division.

Example:

$9\overline{)63}$ with 7 above

63 is the dividend.

The number left over after dividing two numbers that are not evenly divisible.

Example:

$5\overline{)43}$ with $8\ R3$ above

The remainder is 3.

The number you divide by in division.

Example:

$9\overline{)63}$ with 7 above

9 is the divisor.

underestimate

Make an estimate that is
too small.

Name _____

Division Vocabulary and Models

Although multiplication and division are inverse operations, each operation has its own language.

Multiplication Words

$$\begin{array}{r} 3 \leftarrow \boxed{\text{Factor}} \\ \times\ 4 \leftarrow \boxed{\text{Factor}} \\ \hline 12 \leftarrow \boxed{\text{Product}} \end{array}$$

$$\boxed{\text{Factor}} \rightarrow \begin{array}{r} 3 \\ 4\overline{)12} \leftarrow \boxed{\text{Product}} \\ -12 \\ \hline 0 \end{array}$$

Division Words

$$\boxed{\text{Divisor}}\ \begin{array}{r} 3 \leftarrow \boxed{\text{Quotient}} \\ 4\overline{)12} \leftarrow \boxed{\text{Dividend}} \\ -12 \\ \hline 0 \end{array}$$

The models for multiplication and division are the same models.

array

rows and columns

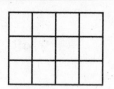

area model

___ ft

| 3 ft | 12 sq ft |

12 bottles on a table

$12 \div 3 =$ _____

$3 \times$ _____ $= 12$

12 tiles on a wall

$12 \div 3 =$ _____

$3 \times$ _____ $= 12$

12 square feet of carpet

$12 \div 3 =$ _____

$3 \times$ _____ $= 12$

Discuss Remainders

Sometimes when you divide, some are left over. The left over amount is called the **remainder**.

If you have 14 juice boxes arranged in groups of 3, how many juice boxes will be left over?

$$\begin{array}{r} 4\ \text{R2} \\ 3\overline{)14} \\ -12 \\ \hline 2 \end{array}$$

← 2 are left over.
2 is the remainder.

Compare the divisor and the remainder. The remainder must be less than the divisor.

$2 < 3$, so the remainder is correct.

Multiply to check division. Add the remainder.

$4 \times 3 = 12$

$12 + 2 = 14$

Divide with Remainders

The remainder must be less than the divisor.
If it is not, increase the quotient.

$$
\begin{array}{r}
3 \\
5\overline{)23} \\
-15 \\
\hline
8 \text{ no} \\
8 > 5
\end{array}
\longrightarrow
\begin{array}{r}
4 \text{ R3} \\
5\overline{)23} \\
-20 \\
\hline
3 \text{ yes} \\
3 < 5
\end{array}
$$

$$
\begin{array}{r}
8 \\
9\overline{)87} \\
-72 \\
\hline
15 \text{ no} \\
15 > 9
\end{array}
\longrightarrow
\begin{array}{r}
9 \text{ R6} \\
9\overline{)87} \\
-81 \\
\hline
6 \text{ yes} \\
6 < 9
\end{array}
$$

Divide with remainders.

1 $2\overline{)19}$ **2** $7\overline{)50}$ **3** $9\overline{)48}$

Divide. Multiply to check the last problem in each row.

4 $6\overline{)27}$ **5** $4\overline{)30}$ **6** $\begin{array}{r} 5 \text{ R4} \\ 7\overline{)39} \\ -35 \\ \hline 4 \end{array}$ $\begin{array}{l} 7 \cdot 5 + 4 = \\ 35 + 4 = 39 \end{array}$

7 $8\overline{)43}$ **8** $5\overline{)26}$ **9** $9\overline{)41}$

10 $5\overline{)32}$ **11** $4\overline{)21}$ **12** $3\overline{)22}$

Multiply and Divide with Zeros

When you multiply or divide with zeros, you can see a pattern.

$4 \times 1 = 4$	$4 \div 4 = 1$	$7 \times 5 = 35$	$35 \div 7 = 5$
$4 \times 10 = 40$	$40 \div 4 = 10$	$7 \times 50 = 350$	$350 \div 7 = 50$
$4 \times 100 = 400$	$400 \div 4 = 100$	$7 \times 500 = 3,500$	$3,500 \div 7 = 500$
$4 \times 1,000 = 4,000$	$4,000 \div 4 = 1,000$	$7 \times 5,000 = 35,000$	$35,000 \div 7 = 5,000$

13 What pattern do you notice when you multiply with zeros?

_____

_____

14 What pattern do you notice when you divide with zeros?

_____

_____

Find the unknown factor. Multiply to check the division.

15 $4\overline{)320}$ $4 \cdot$ _____ $= 320$ **16** $6\overline{)420}$ $6 \cdot$ _____ $= 420$

17 $7\overline{)49}$ $7 \cdot$ _____ $= 49$ **18** $3\overline{)1,800}$ $3 \cdot$ _____ $= 1,800$

19 $5\overline{)4,500}$ $5 \cdot$ _____ $= 4,500$ **20** $9\overline{)3,600}$ $9 \cdot$ _____ $= 3,600$

21 $6\overline{)3,000}$ $6 \cdot$ _____ $= 3,000$ **22** $5\overline{)4,000}$ $5 \cdot$ _____ $= 4,000$

Divide with Zeros and Remainders

Divide. Multiply to check your answer.

23
$$\begin{array}{r} 300 \text{ R6} \\ 7\overline{\smash{)}2{,}106} \\ -2{,}100 \\ \hline 6 \end{array}$$

24 8)643

25 9)275

26 2)1,601

27 3)1,802

28 4)2,803

29 5)4,503

30 6)4,205

 Check Understanding

Make a drawing to show 4)14. Your drawing should show an array and a remainder.

Divide with Remainders

Multiplying and Dividing

Complete the steps.

1 Sam divides <u>738 by 6</u>. He uses the Place Value
Sections Method and the Expanded Notation Method.

a. Sam thinks: I'll draw the Place Value Sections that I know from
multiplication. To divide, I need to find how many hundreds,
tens, and ones to find the unknown factor.

Place Value Sections Method   **Expanded Notation Method**

_100_ hundreds + _a_ tens + _3_ ones

$\underline{1}00$ $\underline{2}0$ 2

6	738		

$6\overline{)738}$

b. 6 × 100 = 600 will fit. 6 × 200 = 1,200 is too big.

$\overset{|}{1}00$ + $2$0   + 10

6	738		

$6\overline{)738}$

c. I have 138 left for the other sections.
6 × 20 = 120 will fit. 6 × 30 = 180 is too big.

100   + $2$0   + 10

6	738 −600	138	

138

$$\begin{array}{r} 100 \\ 6\overline{)738} \\ -600 \\ \hline 138 \end{array}$$

d. 6 × 3 = 18

100   +   20   +   ___   =   _____

6	738 −600	138 −120	18

138   18   0

$$\begin{array}{r} \left.\begin{array}{r} 20 \\ 100 \end{array}\right] \\ 6\overline{)738} \\ -600 \\ \hline 138 \\ -120 \\ \hline 18 \end{array}$$

Practice the Place Value Sections Method

Solve. Use Place Value Sections Method for division.

The area of the new rectangular sidewalk at the mall will be 3,915 square feet. It will be 9 feet wide. How long will it be? __435 ft__

```
        400  +   30  +   5   = 435
      ┌────────┬───────┬───────┐
   9  │ 3,915  │  315  │  45   │
   ft │ −3,600 │ −270  │ −45   │
      └────────┴───────┴───────┘
         315      45      0
```

✓

② The rectangular sidewalk at the theater will have an area of 2,748 square feet. It will be 6 feet wide. How long will it be? __458__

yes I w

```
      4 00  +   5 0  +   8   = 458
    ┌────────┬───────┬───────┐
    │  2748  │  348  │  48   │
  6 │  2400  │  300  │  48   │
    │   348  │   48  │   0   │
    └────────┴───────┴───────┘
```

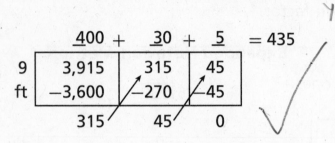

③ Pens are packaged in boxes of 8. The store received a shipment of 4,576 pens. How many boxes of pens did they receive? __572__

```
       500  +  10  +   2   = 572
     ┌───────┬──────┬──────┐
   8 │ 4576  │ 576  │ 16   │
     │ 4000  │ 560  │ 16   │
     │  576  │  16  │  0   │
     └───────┴──────┴──────┘
```

④ A factory has 2,160 erasers. They package them in groups of 5. How many packages of erasers does the factory have? __432__

```
       400  +   30  +   2   = 432
     ┌───────┬───────┬──────┐
   5 │ 2160  │  160  │ 10   │
     │ 2000  │  150  │ 10   │
     │  160  │   10  │  0   │
     └───────┴───────┴──────┘
```

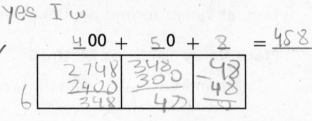

⑤ A party planner has 834 small flowers to make party favors. She will put 3 flowers in each party favor. How many party favors can she make? __2 178__

```
       800  +  0  +  0   = 234
     ┌──────┬──────┬──────┐
   3 │ 834  │  234 │ 234  │
     │ 600  │   0  │  0   │
     │ 234  │  234 │ 234  │
     └──────┴──────┴──────┘
```

⑥ An artist has 956 tiles to use in a design. He plans to arrange the tiles in groups of 4 tiles. How many groups of 4 tiles can he make?

239

```
       200  +   30  +  4   = ___
     ┌──────┬──────┬──────┐
   4 │ 956  │      │      │
     └──────┴──────┴──────┘
```

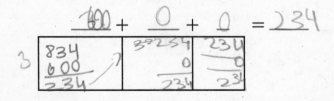

Relate Three-Digit Multiplication to Division

Problem Solving with Three-Digit Quotients

Solve using the Expanded Notation Method for division.

7 A toy company has 740 games to donate to different schools. Each school will receive 4 games. How many schools will receive games?

_____

$\overline{)}$

8 A landscape architect designs a rectangular garden that is 1,232 square feet. It is 8 feet wide. How long is the garden?

_____

$\overline{)}$

9 The convention center is expecting 1,434 people for an event. Since each table can seat 6 people, how many tables will the convention center need to set up?

_____

$\overline{)}$

10 An adult lion weighs 375 pounds. A lion cub weighs 3 pounds. How many times the lion cub's weight is the adult lion's weight?

_____

$\overline{)}$

Practice with the Expanded Notation Method

Solve using the Expanded Notation Method for division.

⑪ 3$\overline{)552}$ ⑫ 7$\overline{)851}$ ⑬ 2$\overline{)978}$

---

⑭ 4$\overline{)979}$ ⑮ 3$\overline{)1,098}$ ⑯ 5$\overline{)2,945}$

---

⑰ 7$\overline{)1,652}$ ⑱ 6$\overline{)3,938}$

Check Understanding

Explain how to relate multiplication to division using the Place Value Sections Method and the Expanded Notation Method.

Relate Three-Digit Multiplication to Division

Name _____

Two-Digit and Four-Digit Quotients

Solve. Use the Place Value Sections and the Expanded Notation Methods for division.

①
$$20 + 8 = 28$$

9	252 ⟋ 72
	− 180 ⟍ − 72

72   0

$$9\overline{)252}$$

②
$$\_0 + \_ = \_$$

6	162	

$$6\overline{)162}$$

Denomanator x
equelvtint x
numinator ÷
6thos

③
$$\_,000 + \_00 + \_0 + \_ = \_\_\_\_$$

8	8,984			

$$8\overline{)8,984}$$

④
$$\_,000 + \_00 + \_0 + \_ = \_\_\_\_$$

3	7,722			

$$3\overline{)7,722}$$

Finding Group Size

5 An orchard has 516 apples ready for delivery. There are the same number of apples in each of 4 crates. How many apples are in each crate?

$516 \div 4 = ?$

4 groups

$$4\overline{)516}$$

Divide 5 hundreds, 1 ten, 6 ones equally among 4 groups.

Complete the steps.

Step 1

4 groups

1 hundred
1 hundred
1 hundred
1 hundred

5 hundreds ÷ 4

Each group gets 1 hundred. 1 hundred is left.

$$\begin{array}{r} 1 \\ 4\overline{)516} \\ -\ 4 \\ \hline 1 \end{array}$$

Regroup 1 hundred.

10 tens + 1 ten = 11 _____

$$\begin{array}{r} 1 \\ 4\overline{)516} \\ -\ 4 \\ \hline 11 \end{array}$$

Step 2

4 groups

1 hundred + 2 tens
1 hundred + 2 tens
1 hundred + 2 tens
1 hundred + 2 tens

11 tens ÷ 4

Each group gets 2 tens. 3 _____ are left.

$$\begin{array}{r} 12 \\ 4\overline{)516} \\ -\ 4 \\ \hline 11 \\ -\ 8 \\ \hline 3 \end{array}$$

Regroup 3 tens.

30 ones + 6 ones = _____ ones

$$\begin{array}{r} 12 \\ 4\overline{)516} \\ -\ 4 \\ \hline 11 \\ -\ 8 \\ \hline 36 \end{array}$$

Step 3

4 groups

1 hundred + 2 tens + 9
1 hundred + 2 tens + 9
1 hundred + 2 tens + 9
1 hundred + 2 tens + 9

36 ones ÷ 4

Each group gets 9 ones. There are _____ ones left.

$$\begin{array}{r} 129 \\ 4\overline{)516} \\ -\ 4 \\ \hline 11 \\ -\ 8 \\ \hline 36 \\ -\ 36 \\ \hline 0 \end{array}$$

There are _____ apples in each crate.

Discuss Two-Digit and Four-Digit Quotients

Name _Sidra S_

Practice

2,5,10,100 ?

Divide.

6 4)868

    217
    600
    800
    2400
    2468
    800
    1668
    600
    1068

7 6)5,142

    857
    200 1,200
    300 3,942
    30   1,800
    50   2,142
         1,800
         342

    1200
    3942

8 3)4,395

    5000

9 4)332

10 7)1,617

11 7)939

12 2)4,276

13 6)2,576

14 7)441

    83 + 84
       HW

15 9)3,735

16 7)406

17 3)9,954

Division Word Problems

Solve.

Show your work.

18 What is the length of a rectangle with an area of 756 square centimeters and a width of 4 centimeters?

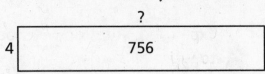

_____

19 At a county fair, there are 7 booths that sell raffle tickets. In one day, 4,592 tickets were sold. Each booth sold the same number of tickets. How many tickets did each booth sell?

_____

20 One part of a city football stadium has 5,688 seats. The seats are arranged in 9 sections. Each section has the same number of seats. How many seats are in each section?

_____

21 An art museum has a total of 475 paintings hanging in 5 different viewing rooms. If each room has the same number of paintings, how many paintings are in each room?

_____

22 A parking garage can hold a total of 762 cars. The same number of cars can park on each floor. There are 6 floors. How many cars can park on each floor?

_____

 Check Understanding

For Problem 22, draw a model like the three-step model shown on page 146.

Discuss Two-Digit and Four-Digit Quotients

The Digit-by-Digit Method

1 Suppose Judith wants to divide 948 by 4. She knows how to use the Place Value Sections Method and the Expanded Notation Method, but she doesn't want to write all the zeros.

Place Value Sections Method

$$200 + \quad 30 + \quad 7 = 237$$

	948	148	28
4	− 800	− 120	− 28
	148	28	0

Expanded Notation Method

$$\begin{array}{r} 7 \\ 30 \\ 200 \end{array} \Big] 237$$

$$4\overline{)948}$$
$$\underline{-800}$$
$$148$$
$$\underline{-120}$$
$$28$$
$$\underline{-28}$$
$$0$$

Judith thinks: I'll look at the place values in decreasing order. I'll imagine zeros in the other places, but I don't need to think about them until I'm ready to divide in that place.

Step 1: Look at the greatest place value first. Divide the hundreds. Then subtract.

9 hundreds ÷ 4 = 2 hundreds + 1 hundred left over

$$\begin{array}{r} 2 \\ 4\overline{)948} \\ \underline{-8} \\ 1 \end{array}$$

Step 2: Bring down the 4. Divide the tens. Then subtract.

14 tens ÷ 4 = 3 tens + 2 tens left over

$$\begin{array}{r} 23 \\ 4\overline{)948} \\ \underline{-8}\downarrow \\ 14 \\ \underline{-12} \\ 2 \end{array}$$

Step 3: Bring down the 8. Divide the ones. Then subtract.

28 ones ÷ 4 = 7 ones

$$\begin{array}{r} 237 \\ 4\overline{)948} \\ \underline{-8} \\ 14 \\ \underline{-12}\downarrow \\ 28 \\ \underline{-28} \\ 0 \end{array}$$

What's the Error?

Dear Math Students,

Here is a division problem I tried to solve.

$$
\begin{array}{r}
5{,}796 \\
3\overline{)1{,}738} \\
-15 \\
\hline
23 \\
-21 \\
\hline
28 \\
-27 \\
\hline
18 \\
-18 \\
\hline
0
\end{array}
$$

Is my answer correct? If not, please help me understand why it is wrong.

Thank you,
Puzzled Penguin

2 Write a response to Puzzled Penguin.

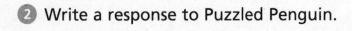

_____

_____

Solve. Use the Digit-by-Digit Method.

3 4$\overline{)3{,}036}$ **4** 7$\overline{)5{,}292}$ **5** 6$\overline{)853}$

Digit-by-Digit Method

Name _____

Practice

Divide.

6 $5\overline{)965}$ **7** $8\overline{)128}$ **8** $8\overline{)928}$

9 $3\overline{)716}$ **10** $4\overline{)4,596}$ **11** $4\overline{)982}$

12 $3\overline{)6,342}$ **13** $8\overline{)578}$ **14** $5\overline{)1,155}$

15 $6\overline{)3,336}$ **16** $7\overline{)672}$ **17** $3\overline{)4,152}$

       Digit-by-Digit Method **151**

Solve Division Problems

**Write an equation to represent the problem.
Then, solve.**

Show your work.

⑱ What is the length of a rectangle with an
area of 528 square centimeters and a width
of 6 centimeters?

```
          ? cm
      ┌──────────────┐
6 cm  │  528 sq cm   │
      └──────────────┘
```

_____

⑲ A cookbook features 414 recipes. There are
3 recipes on each page. How many pages are
in the cookbook?

_____

⑳ A bus travels the same route once a day for
5 days. At the end of the fifth day, the bus has
traveled 435 miles. How many miles does the
bus travel each day?

_____

㉑ Ms. Tyler places a container of marbles at each
table of 6 students. The students are told to
share the marbles equally with the students
at their table. If there are 714 marbles in the
container, how many marbles should each
student get?

_____

㉒ Sam's Used Bookstore is organizing their books
on display shelves. They have 976 books and
want 8 books displayed on each shelf. How
many shelves will the books fill?

_____

✓ **Check Understanding**

Describe how to solve a division problem using the
Digit-by-Digit Method.

Digit-by-Digit Method

Compare Methods

Ellie, José, and Wanda each use their favorite method to solve 1,194 ÷ 5. Discuss the methods.

Ellie's Place Value Sections Method	José's Expanded Notation Method	Wanda's Digit-by-Digit Method

Ellie's Place Value Sections Method

$$200 + 30 + 8 = 238 \text{ R4}$$

	1,194	194	44
5	−1,000	−150	−40
	194	44	4

José's Expanded Notation Method

$$\begin{array}{r} 8 \\ 30 \\ 200 \end{array} \Big] 238 \text{ R4}$$

$$5\overline{)1,194}$$
$$\underline{-\,1,000}$$
$$194$$
$$\underline{-\,150}$$
$$44$$
$$\underline{-\,40}$$
$$4$$

Wanda's Digit-by-Digit Method

$$\begin{array}{r} 238 \text{ R4} \\ 5\overline{)1,194} \\ \underline{-\,1\,0} \\ 19 \\ \underline{-\,15} \\ 44 \\ \underline{-\,40} \\ 4 \end{array}$$

Use any method to solve.

1. $3,248 \div 5 =$ _____

2. $5,847 \div 6 =$ _____

Solve. Use any method.

3. $5\overline{)8,435}$ 4. $3\overline{)2,604}$ 5. $4\overline{)6,738}$ 6. $5\overline{)9,714}$

Division Practice

Use any method to solve.

7 6)2,238   **8** 5)2,431   **9** 7)2,198   **10** 8)2,512

11 4)5,027   **12** 5)5,624   **13** 9)3,631   **14** 6)6,305

What's the Error?

Dear Math Students,

This is a problem from my math homework. My teacher says my answer is not correct, but I can't figure out what I did wrong. Can you help me find and fix my mistake?

Your friend,
Puzzled Penguin

```
      7,069 R2
   5)3,847
   − 35
      34
   − 30
      47
   − 45
       2
```

15 Write a response to Puzzled Penguin.

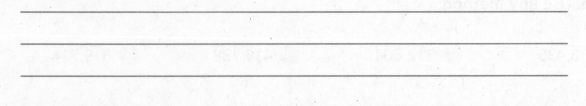

_____

_____

_____

_____

Check Understanding

Describe the advantages and disadvantages of the three division methods used in this lesson.

Relate Three Methods

Practice Division

Use any method to solve.

1 $8\overline{)960}$

2 $4\overline{)632}$

3 $7\overline{)809}$

4 $5\overline{)736}$

5 $4\overline{)3,068}$

6 $3\overline{)6,206}$

7 $2\overline{)6,476}$

8 $6\overline{)8,825}$

Solve Division Word Problems

9 A helper in the school store suggests selling notebooks in packages of 4. How many packages of 4 can be made from 192 notebooks?

_____

10 Another helper suggests selling notebooks in packages of 6. How many packages of 6 can be made from 192 notebooks?

_____

11 The store will sell packages of notebooks for $3.00 each.

a. Which would be a better deal for students, packages of 4 or packages of 6?

_____

_____

b. Which package size would make more money for the store?

_____

_____

Solve Division Word Problems (continued)

Another helper in the school store suggests making packages of 7 or 8 notebooks.

Show your work.

12 How many packages of 7 notebooks can be made from 896 notebooks? _____

13 How many packages of 8 notebooks can be made from 896 notebooks? _____

14 The store will sell packages of notebooks for $6.00 each.

a. Would you rather buy a package with 7 notebooks or a package with 8 notebooks? Explain.

_____

_____

b. Would packages of 7 notebooks or packages of 8 notebooks make more money for the store? Explain.

_____

_____

15 The students at Walnut Street School collected 2,790 cans for a recycling center. Each student brought in 5 cans. How many students attend the school?

_____

16 A cube can be made from 6 square cards that are each the same size. How many cubes can be made out of 7,254 cards?

_____

17 There are 5,896 beads in a barrel at a factory. These beads will be sold in packets of 4. How many full packets can be made from the beads in the barrel?

_____

✓ **Check Understanding**

Solve the problem 6,584 ÷ 8 using any one of the methods discussed in this lesson. Explain your steps. _____

Divide by Any Method

Name _____

What's the Error?

Dear Math Students,

I started to solve this division problem and realized there was a problem. Some friends suggested different ways to fix it.

Your friend,
Puzzled Penguin

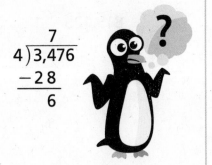

$$4\overline{)3{,}476}$$
$$-28$$
$$\quad 6$$

Jacob suggested that Puzzled Penguin erase the 7 and write 8 in its place. Puzzled Penguin would also need to erase the calculations and do them over.

$$
\begin{array}{r}
8 \\
4\overline{)3{,}476} \\
-32 \\
\hline
2
\end{array}
$$

Fred told Puzzled Penguin to cross out the 7 and write 8 above it. The next step would be to subtract one more 4.

$$
\begin{array}{r}
8 \\
\cancel{7} \\
4\overline{)3{,}476} \\
-28 \\
\hline
6 \\
-4
\end{array}
$$

Amad showed Puzzled Penguin how to use the Expanded Notation Method and just keep going.

$$
\begin{array}{r}
100 \\
700 \\
4\overline{)3{,}476} \\
-2{,}800 \\
\hline
676 \\
-400 \\
\hline
276
\end{array}
$$

Kris showed Puzzled Penguin how, with the Place Value Sections Method, another section can be added.

	700 +	100
4	3,476	676
	−2,800	−400
	676	276

---

1 What was Puzzled Penguin's problem?

_____

2 Discuss the solutions above. Which friend was right?

_____

Zeros in Quotients

3 6)1,842   **4** 8)5,125   **5** 4)4,152   **6** 5)9,522

7 3)7,531   **8** 2)4,018   **9** 4)8,200   **10** 7)9,102

11 Cameron has a collection of 436 miniature cars that he displays on 4 shelves in a bookcase. If the cars are divided equally among the shelves, how many cars are on each shelf?

Show your work.

_____

12 The Tropical Tour Company has 2,380 brochures to distribute equally among its 7 resort hotels. How many brochures will each hotel receive?

_____

13 A factory packs 8,440 bottles of water in boxes each day. If each box contains 8 bottles, how many full boxes of water can the factory pack in one day?

_____

 Check Understanding
Describe how you would adjust a quotient when an estimated digit is too low.

Just-Under Quotient Digits

Check Quotients With Rounding and Estimation

Rounding and estimating can be used to check answers.
Review your rounding skills, and then apply what you know
to division problems.

**Use rounding and estimating to decide whether each
quotient makes sense.**

1 $3\overline{)56}$ 18 R2   **2** $5\overline{)463}$ 92 R3   **3** $6\overline{)5,568}$ 928   **4** $7\overline{)907}$ 129 R4

Practice Dividing and Estimating

**Solve, using any method. Then check your answer by
rounding and estimating.**

5 $7\overline{)59}$ **6** $3\overline{)72}$ **7** $6\overline{)83}$

8 $7\overline{)628}$ **9** $7\overline{)805}$ **10** $8\overline{)869}$

11 $2\overline{)2,986}$ **12** $6\overline{)4,652}$ **13** $7\overline{)7,310}$

Estimate or Exact Answer

Some problems require an exact answer. Others require
an estimate only.

Exact Answer If a problem asks for an exact answer, then you will have to do the calculation. **Example:** The school cafeteria prepares 3,210 lunches each week. The same number of lunches are prepared 5 days each week. How many lunches are prepared each day? Discuss why you think this problem requires an exact answer.	**Estimate** If a problem asks for a close answer and uses *about, approximately, almost,* or *nearly,* then you can estimate. **Example:** Milo has to read a 229-page book. He has 8 days to finish it. About how many pages should he read each day? Discuss why an estimate, and not an exact answer, is appropriate.

**Decide whether you need an exact answer or an estimate.
Then find the answer.**

14 Sam bought a board that was
72 inches long to make
bookshelves. He wants to cut the
board into three equal pieces and
use each one for a shelf. How long
will each shelf be?

_____

15 Carl's mother baked 62 mini
muffins for Carl's class. There are
18 people in his class, including
the teacher. About how many mini
muffins should each person get?

_____

16 Each 24-inch shelf can hold about
10 books. Approximately how
many inches wide is each book?

_____

17 Malcom wants to buy 3 train
tickets. Each ticket costs $45.
How much money will he need?

_____

✔ **Check Understanding**
Describe one rounding method you used to estimate answers in this lesson.

Different Kinds of Remainders

Remainders in division have different meanings, depending upon the type of problem you solve.

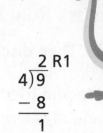

$$\begin{array}{r} 2\ \text{R}1 \\ 4\overline{)9} \\ -8 \\ \hline 1 \end{array}$$

The same numeric solution shown at the right works for the following five problems. Describe why the remainder means something different in each problem.

A. **The remainder is not part of the question.** Thomas has one 9-foot pine board. He needs to make 4-foot shelves for his books. How many shelves can he cut?

_____
_____
_____
_____

B. **The remainder causes the answer to be rounded up.** Nine students are going on a field trip. Parents have offered to drive. If each parent can drive 4 students, how many parents need to drive?

_____
_____
_____
_____

C. **The remainder is a fractional part of the answer.** One Monday Kim brought 9 apples to school. She shared them equally among herself and 3 friends. How many apples did each person get?

_____
_____
_____
_____

D. **The remainder is a decimal part of the answer.** Raul bought 4 toy cars for $9.00. Each car costs the same amount. How much did each car cost?

_____
_____
_____

E. **The remainder is the only part needed to answer the question.** Nine students have signed up to run a relay race. If each relay team can have 4 runners, how many students cannot run in the race?

_____
_____
_____
_____

© Houghton Mifflin Harcourt Publishing Company

Discuss Real World Division Problems

Solve. Then discuss the meaning of the remainder.

1 Maddie tried to divide 160 stickers equally among herself and 5 friends. There were some stickers left over, so she kept them. How many stickers did Maddie get?

_____

_____

_____

_____

2 Kendra bought a bag of 200 cheese crackers for her class. If each student gets 7 crackers, how many students are there? How many crackers are left over?

_____

_____

_____

_____

3 Jerry bought shelves to hold the 132 DVDs in his collection. Each shelf can fit 8 DVDs. How many full shelves will Jerry have?

_____

_____

_____

4 Racheed had 87 pennies. He divided them equally among his 4 sisters. How many pennies did Racheed have left after he gave his sisters their shares?

_____

_____

_____

5 Mara wants to buy some new pencil boxes for her pencil collection. She has 47 pencils. If each pencil box holds 9 pencils, how many pencil boxes does Mara need to buy?

_____

_____

_____

6 Henry's coin bank holds only nickels. Henry takes $4.42 to the bank to exchange for nickels only. How many nickels will he get from the bank?

_____

_____

_____

✓**Check Understanding**

How do you know what to do with the remainder when you divide?

Make Sense of Remainders

Mixed One-Step Word Problems

The fourth- and fifth-grade classes at Jackson Elementary School held a Just-for-Fun Winter Carnival. All of the students in the school were invited.

Decide what operation you need to use to solve each problem. Then solve the problem.

1 Two students from each fourth- and fifth-grade class were on the planning committee. If there were a total of 14 classes for the two grades, how many students planned the carnival?

_____

_____

2 To advertise the carnival, students decorated 4 hallway bulletin boards. They started with 2,025 pieces of colored paper. When they finished, they had 9 pieces left. How many pieces of paper did they use?

_____

_____

3 The parents ordered pizzas to serve at the carnival. Each pizza was cut into 8 slices. How many pizzas had to be ordered so that 1,319 people could each have one slice?

_____

_____

4 There were 822 students signed up to run in timed races. If exactly 6 students ran in each race, how many races were there?

_____

_____

5 At the raffle booth, 364 fourth-graders each bought one ticket to win a new school supply set. Only 8 fifth-graders each bought a ticket. How many students bought raffle tickets altogether?

_____

_____

6 Altogether, 1,263 students were enrolled in the first through fifth grades at Jackson School. On the day of the carnival, 9 students were absent. How many students could have participated in the carnival activities?

_____

_____

Mixed Multistep Word Problems

Solve these problems about Pine Street School's Games Day.

7 At the start of the games, 193 fourth-graders signed up to play in three events. Eighty-seven played in the first event. The rest of the students were evenly divided between the second and third events. How many students played in the third event?

_____

_____

8 Three teams stacked paper cups into pyramids. Each team had 176 cups to use. Team 1 used exactly half of their cups. Team 2 used four times as many cups as Team 3. Team 3 used 32 cups. Which team stacked the most cups?

_____

_____

9 A team from each school had 250 foam balls and a bucket. The Jackson team dunked 6 fewer balls than the Pine Street team. The Pine Street team dunked all but 8 of their balls. How many balls did the two teams dunk in all?

_____

_____

_____

10 When the day was over, everybody had earned at least 1 medal, and 32 students each got 2 medals. In all, 194 each of gold, silver, and bronze medals were given out. How many students played in the games?

_____

_____

_____

Check Understanding

In Problem 8, find which team stacked the most cups if each team had 260 cups to use.

_____

_____

Division and Amusement Parks

There are many things to do at an amusement park: ride the rides, play some games, try new foods. Many people like to ride roller coasters while at the amusement park.

The top three tallest roller coasters in the world are in the United States. One of the tallest roller coasters is 456 feet tall and is located in Jackson, New Jersey.

The fourth and fifth grade classes went on a field trip to the amusement park.

Show your work.

1 There are 58 fourth-grade students who are in line to ride the Loop-the-Loop roller coaster. Each roller coaster car holds 4 people. How many roller coaster cars are needed so they all can ride the roller coaster at the same time?

_____

2 Forty-one people are riding the Mile Long wooden roller coaster. Each roller coaster car holds 6 people. All the cars are full except the last car. How many people are in the last car?

_____

More Amusement Park Fun

After riding the roller coasters, the fourth and fifth grade classes spend the rest of the day getting lunch, going shopping, and riding the rest of the rides at the amusement park.

Solve.

Show your work.

3 There are 27 students in Evan's group. Each student decides to get a lunch special at the food stand. If each lunch special is $7, how much did the students spend for lunch altogether?

_____

4 Thirty-one students are in line to ride the Ferris wheel. Four students are needed to fill each Ferris wheel car. How many Ferris wheel cars will be full?

_____

5 In the souvenir shop, a worker opens a box of posters. The posters in the box are bundled in groups of 8. There are a total of 2,864 posters in a box. How many bundles of posters are in the box?

_____

Focus on Problem Solving

Use rounding and estimation to decide whether the quotient makes sense.

$$\begin{array}{r} 52 \text{ R4} \\ 7\overline{)368} \end{array}$$

①

_____

_____

Use any method to divide.

② $4\overline{)8,392}$

③ $5\overline{)6,037}$

Solve.

Show your work.

④ It takes 9 tickets to ride a Ferris wheel. Luis has 158 tickets. How many times can Luis ride the Ferris wheel?

_____

⑤ Puzzles are packaged in groups of 3. If the store has 183 nature puzzles and 165 animal puzzles, how many packages of puzzles are there?

_____

_____

Name _____ Date _____

Add or subtract.

1   333
      + 270

2   87,827
      − 79,363

3   568
      − 197

4   19,785
      + 9,512

5   4,329
      − 3,110

6   987
      − 162

7   48,096
      − 2,168

8   799,780
      + 993,903

9   941,259
      − 398,739

10 39,740
      + 96,510

11 8,624
      + 7,813

12 1,460
      + 4,541

13 342,824
      − 96,590

14 8,461
      + 197

15 212
      + 614

Name _____

Experiment with Two-Digit Divisors

Milo sold coupon books for a fundraiser. Each coupon book had 32 coupons. If Milo sold a total of 448 coupons, how many coupon books did he sell?

Rectangle Model

?

32 | 448

To find the number of coupon books, divide 448 by 32.

Discuss how these division methods are alike and different.

Digit-by-Digit

Step 1

$$32 \overline{)\,448}$$
(30)

Round the divisor.

Step 2

$$\begin{array}{r} 1 \\ 32 \overline{)\,448} \\ (30) \end{array}$$

Estimate the first digit:

30 divides into 40 about 1 time.

Step 3

$$\begin{array}{r} 1 \\ 32 \overline{)\,448} \\ (30) -32 \\ \hline 128 \end{array}$$

Multiply and subtract. Bring down 8 ones.

Step 4

$$\begin{array}{r} 14 \\ 32 \overline{)\,448} \\ (30) -32 \\ \hline 128 \\ -128 \end{array}$$

Estimate the next digit and multiply.

Expanded Notation

Step 1

$$32 \overline{)\,448}$$
(30)

Round the divisor.

Step 2

$$\begin{array}{r} 10 \\ 32 \overline{)\,448} \\ (30) \end{array}$$

Estimate the first number:

30 divides into 400 about 10 times.

Step 3

$$\begin{array}{r} 10 \\ 32 \overline{)\,448} \\ (30) -320 \\ \hline 128 \end{array}$$

Multiply and subtract.

10 • 32 = 320

Step 4

$$\begin{array}{r} 4 \} 14 \\ 10 \\ 32 \overline{)\,448} \\ (30) -320 \\ \hline 128 \\ -128 \end{array}$$

Estimate the next number and multiply.

Place Value Sections

Step 1

10

32 (30) | 448

Round the divisor and estimate the first number.

Step 2

10

32 (30) | 448 − 320 → 128

Multiply and subtract.

Step 3

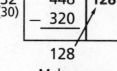

10 +

32 (30) | 448 − 320 → 128 | 128

Make a new section.

Step 4

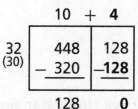

10 + 4

32 (30) | 448 − 320 → 128 | 128 − 128 → 0

Estimate the next number, and multiply and subtract.

Experiment with Two-Digit Divisors (continued)

Look at Exercises 1–3. Would you round the divisor up or down to estimate the first digit of the quotient? Complete each exercise, using any method you choose.

1 $28\overline{)403}$ **2** $41\overline{)861}$ **3** $33\overline{)726}$

Does Estimation Always Work?

Complete Exercise 4 as a class. Does rounding give you a correct estimate of the first digit? Does it give you a correct estimate of the next digit? Discuss what you can do to finish the problem.

4 $14\overline{)306}$

Complete and discuss each exercise below. Use any method you choose.

5 $13\overline{)559}$ **6** $13\overline{)209}$ **7** $54\overline{)692}$

✓ **Check Understanding**

Which division method did you use to solve Exercise 5? Explain your reasoning.

Explore Two-Digit Divisors

Underestimating

Here are two ways to divide 764 ÷ 15. Discuss each method and answer the questions as a class.

```
      (20)  4
         15)764
          -60
           16  ←  What does
                   this number
                   tell us?
```

```
              10  ←  What does
      (20) 40          this number
         15)764         tell us?
          -600
           164
```

How do we know that the first estimated number is not right? What number should we try next? Solve the problem using that number.

How do we know that the first estimated number is not right this time? Do we need to erase, or can we just finish solving the problem? Try it.

1 When we estimate with a number that is too big (**overestimate**), we have to erase and change the number. When we estimate with a number that is too small (**underestimate**), do we always have to erase? Explain your answer.

_____

_____

_____

_____

Solve each division. You may need to adjust one or both of the estimated numbers.

2 28)868

3 17)897

4 18)798

Too High or Too Low?

Think about what kind of divisor is most likely to lead to an estimated number that is wrong. Test your idea by doing the first step of each problem below.

5 $41\overline{)836}$ **6** $34\overline{)623}$ **7** $29\overline{)928}$ **8** $16\overline{)351}$

9 What kind of divisor is most likely to lead to an estimated number that is wrong? How can you adjust for these cases?

_____

_____

Mixed Practice with Adjusted Estimates   *Show your work.*

10 Soccer balls sell for $19 each. This week the store sold $589 worth of soccer balls.

How many soccer balls were sold? _____

11 Daniel is packing 419 tomatoes in crates that hold 24 tomatoes each.

How many crates will Daniel fill? _____

How many tomatoes will be left over? _____

12 The kite club members have 310 meters of string to make 12 kites. They use the same amount of string for each kite.

How many meters of string will each kite have? _____

How many meters of string will be left? _____

✓ **Check Understanding**

If the estimate of the first digit of a quotient is too low, you should try the next _____ digit.

Too Large, Too Small, or Just Right?

Use Compatible Numbers

A plane ticket cost Marla $257. She multiplies by 4 and finds that the cost for her family is $1,028.

$$\begin{array}{r} \$257 \\ \times\ 4 \\ \hline \$1,028 \end{array}$$

To check that her product is reasonable, Marla uses numbers that are easy to compute with mentally, or **compatible numbers**.

"I know that 4 × 250 is 1,000 and 4 × 300 is 1,200. So, my answer 1,028 should be between 1,000 and 1,200. It is."

Terrell has 6 boxes to store 1,470 trading cards. He divides and finds that each box will have 245 cards.

$$6\overline{)1,470}\ \ ^{245}$$

To check that his quotient is reasonable, Terrell uses compatible numbers.

"I know that 1,200 ÷ 6 is 200 and 1,800 ÷ 6 is 300. Because 1,470 is between 1,200 and 1,800, my answer should be between 200 and 300. It is."

Solve. Then use compatible numbers to check the solution.

1. $$\begin{array}{r} 764 \\ \times\ 5 \\ \hline \end{array}$$

2. $$\begin{array}{r} 6,789 \\ \times\ 2 \\ \hline \end{array}$$

3. $6\overline{)4,560}$

4. $8\overline{)7,136}$

5. Yuri delivers 165 newspapers every day of the week. How many newspapers did Yuri deliver last week?

_____

6. Jessica earns $1,233 a month working at the veterinary clinic. She makes $9 an hour. How many hours does Jessica work in a month?

_____

7. A pilot flies the same route 5 times for a total of 1,890 miles. What is the length of her route?

_____

Check Products and Quotients

Dion wants to buy 11 game tickets that cost $17 each. He multiplies and finds the total cost.

$$\$17 \times 11 = \$187$$
$$\downarrow \qquad \downarrow$$
$$\$17 \times 10 = \$170$$

Then he uses mental math and decides that his product is reasonable.

Julia has 728 squares to make a quilt. The quilt design has 26 rows of squares. She divides to find the number of squares in each row.

$$728 \div 26 = 28$$
$$\downarrow \qquad \downarrow$$
$$750 \div 25 = 30$$

Then she uses mental math and decides that her quotient is reasonable.

8 Why do you think Julia used compatible numbers instead of rounding to check her quotient?

_____

Solve. Then use compatible numbers to check the solution.

9   29
     ×16

10   34
      ×21

11 26)‾338‾

12 21)‾441‾

13 Ming Na owns a flower shop. She uses 494 flowers to make 26 centerpieces. How many flowers does she use for each centerpiece if they have the same number of flowers?

_____

14 Jackson wants to buy a set of golf clubs for $308. He plans to pay for the set with 14 monthly payments. How much will each payment be?

_____

✓ **Check Understanding**
Write a pair of compatible numbers you could use to

estimate the quotient for 8,919 ÷ 9.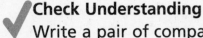

Use Mental Math to Check for Reasonableness

Use any method to divide.

1️⃣ $34\overline{)958}$

2️⃣ $18\overline{)864}$

Solve. Then use compatible numbers to check the solution.

3️⃣ $\begin{array}{r} 459 \\ \times\ \ \ 6 \\ \hline \end{array}$

4️⃣ $6\overline{)2,280}$

5️⃣ There are 864 seats. There are 24 seats in each row. How many rows of seats are there?

_____

Divide.

1 $3 \div 3 = \boxed{}$

2 $8 \div 2 = \boxed{}$

3 $9 \div 3 = \boxed{}$

4 $16 \div 2 = \boxed{}$

5 $25 \div 5 = \boxed{}$

6 $28 \div 4 = \boxed{}$

7 $32 \div 8 = \boxed{}$

8 $40 \div 4 = \boxed{}$

9 $48 \div 6 = \boxed{}$

10 $56 \div 7 = \boxed{}$

11 $63 \div 9 = \boxed{}$

12 $54 \div 6 = \boxed{}$

13 $64 \div 8 = \boxed{}$

14 $72 \div 8 = \boxed{}$

15 $90 \div 9 = \boxed{}$

1 For 1a–1d, choose True or False to indicate if the statement is correct.

1a. $245 \div 6 = 40$ R5   ○ True   ○ False

1b. $803 \div 2 = 400$ ○ True   ○ False

1c. $492 \div 7 = 69$ R7   ○ True   ○ False

1d. $355 \div 5 = 71$ ○ True   ○ False

2 A train has a total of 216 seats in 3 cars. Each train car has the same number of seats. How many seats are in each train car?

_____ seats

3 Kayla puts together gift boxes of fruit to sell at her fruit stand. She places exactly 6 pieces of fruit in each box. She only sells full boxes of fruit.

Part A

Kayla has 256 apples. How many boxes of fruit can she fill? Explain how you found your answer.

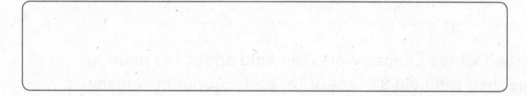

Part B

Kayla has enough peaches to fill 31 gift boxes. How many apples and peaches did Kayla put in gift boxes to sell at her fruit stand? Show your work.

④ Margaret is dividing 829 by 4.

Part A

Explain why Margaret needs to write a zero in the tens place of the quotient.

Part B

How would the digit in the tens place of the quotient change if Margaret were dividing 829 by 2?

⑤ A storage shelf where Carmen works can hold about 165 pounds. The storage shelf can hold 8 boxes of car parts. About how many pounds does each box weigh? Does this problem require an exact answer or an estimate? Then find the answer.

⑥ What is 945 ÷ 45?

Ⓐ 20   Ⓒ 22

Ⓑ 21   Ⓓ 31

7 Divide 4,124 by 2.

8 Joshua carried 52 loads of sand to make a play area. Each load weighed 21 pounds. How many pounds of sand does Joshua use to make the play area? Use the numbers and symbols on the keypad to write the expression needed to solve this problem. Then solve the problem.

7	8	9
4	5	6
1	2	3
0	÷	×

expression: _____

_____ pounds

9 There are 118 boys and 121 girls signed up for a volleyball league. The coaches first make teams of 9 players and then assign any remaining players to make some of the teams have 10 players.

Part A

How many teams of 10 players will there be? Explain.

Part B

How many teams of 9 players will there be? Explain.

⑩ A florist has 2,388 flowers to make into small bouquets. She wants 6 flowers in each bouquet. How many bouquets can she make? Complete the Place Value Sections to solve.

___00   +   ___0   +   ___   =   _____ bouquets

⑪ Divide 840 by 46. Show your work.

⑫ For Exercises 12a–12d, choose Yes or No to tell if the quotient is reasonable.

12a. $\begin{array}{r} 39 \text{ R3} \\ 6\overline{)297} \end{array}$ ○ Yes   ○ No

12b. $\begin{array}{r} 814 \\ 4\overline{)3,256} \end{array}$ ○ Yes   ○ No

12c. $\begin{array}{r} 228 \text{ R5} \\ 8\overline{)4,229} \end{array}$ ○ Yes   ○ No

12d. $\begin{array}{r} 1,007 \text{ R1} \\ 8\overline{)5,136} \end{array}$ ○ Yes   ○ No

13 Hailey finds 24 seashells on Friday and another 38 seashells on Saturday. She shares as many of the seashells as she can equally among herself and 3 friends. She keeps the leftover seashells for herself. How many seashells does Hailey get? Show your work.

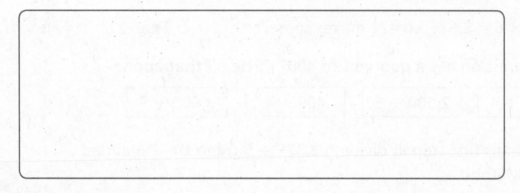

14 Ethan has 203 geodes to put into display cases. Each case holds 8 geodes. How many cases does Ethan need to hold all the geodes? Explain how you know.

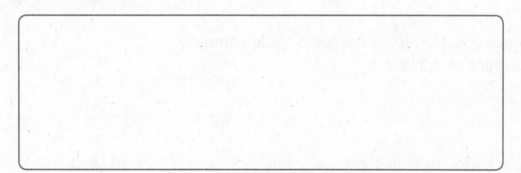

15 Select one number from each column to make the equation true.

$$5,155 \div 3 = \blacksquare \ R \ \blacksquare$$

Quotient	Remainder
○ 1,715	○ 1
○ 1,717	○ 2
○ 1,718	○ 3
○ 1,720	○ 4

16 Julie divided 2,526 by 6 and found a quotient of 421.
For 16a–16c, choose True or False to tell if the
statement is correct.

16a. $2,400 \div 6 = 400$, so 421 is reasonable. ○ True ○ False

16b. $2,526 \div 6 = 421$ R5 ○ True ○ False

16c. $421 \times 6 = 2,526$, so 421 makes sense. ○ True ○ False

17 Which expression has a quotient of 400? Circle all that apply.

| $1,600 \div 4$ | $2,000 \div 5$ | $400 \div 4$ | $3,600 \div 9$ |

18 Kyle wrote his first step in dividing $3,325 \div 5$ using the Expanded
Notation Method.

$$\begin{array}{r} 500 \\ 5\overline{)3,325} \\ -2,500 \\ \hline 825 \end{array}$$

Part A

Write an equation to calculate a reasonable estimate
for the quotient of $3,325 \div 5$.

Part B

Explain how Kyle's division work would be different if he had used
your estimate instead of 500 as his first step. Then find the exact
quotient of $3,325 \div 5$.

© Houghton Mifflin Harcourt Publishing Company

Make a Reading Plan

Matthew has 63 pages to read in 2–5 days. He wants to
read the same number of pages each day and the
greatest number of pages in the fewest days possible.

1 What is the best number of days for Matthew's
reading plan?

_____

_____

2 How did you decide?

_____

_____

_____

_____

Sophia has 131 pages to read in 2–5 days.

3 Would it be possible for her to read the same number of pages
each day? Explain.

_____

_____

_____

4 Sophia decides to read the same number of pages on as
many days as possible. What reading plan could Sophia follow?
Show work to support your answer.

_____

_____

_____

_____

5 Suppose Sophia read 23 pages on the first day. She plans to read the remaining pages in 3–5 days. She wants to read the same number of pages on each of these days and the greatest number of pages in the fewest days possible. What is the best choice for the number of days for Sophia's reading plan? Explain how you decided.

_____

_____

_____

_____

_____

_____

6 Explain how to write your own division problem with any given quotient and remainder. Give an example that includes the relationship between multiplication and division in your explanation.

_____

_____

_____

_____

_____

_____

_____

Dear Family:

In Unit 4 of *Math Expressions,* your child will apply the skills he or she has learned about operations with whole numbers while solving real world problems involving addition, subtraction, multiplication, and division.

Your child will simplify and evaluate expressions. Parentheses will be introduced to show which operation should be done first. The symbols "=" and "≠" will be used to show whether numbers and expressions are equal.

Other topics of study in this unit include situation and solution equations for addition and subtraction, as well as multiplication and division. Your child will use situation equations to represent real world problems and solution equations to solve the problems. This method of representing a problem is particularly helpful when the problems contain greater numbers and students cannot solve mentally.

Your child will also solve multiplication and addition comparison problems and compare these types of problems identifying what is the same or different.

Addition Comparison	**Multiplication Comparison**
Angela is 14 years old. She is 4 years older than Damarcus. How old is Damarcus?	Shawn colored 5 pages in a coloring book. Anja colored 4 times as many pages as Shawn colored. How many pages did Anja color?

Students learn that in the addition problem they are adding 4, while in the multiplication problem, they are multiplying by 4.

Your child will apply this knowledge to solve word problems using all four operations and involving one or more steps.

Finally, your child will find factor pairs for whole numbers and generate and analyze numerical and geometric patterns.

If you have any questions or comments, please contact me.

Sincerely,
Your child's teacher

Estimada familia:

En la Unidad 4 de Math Expressions, su hijo aplicará las destrezas relacionadas con operaciones de números enteros que ha adquirido, resolviendo problemas cotidianos que involucran suma, resta, multiplicación y división.

Su hijo simplificará y evaluará expresiones. Se introducirán los paréntesis como una forma de mostrar cuál operación deberá completarse primero. Los signos "=" y "≠" se usarán para mostrar si los números o las expresiones son iguales o no.

Otros temas de estudio en esta unidad incluyen ecuaciones de situación y de solución para la suma y resta, así como para la multiplicación y división. Su hijo usará ecuaciones de situación para representar problemas de la vida cotidiana y ecuaciones de solución para resolver esos problemas. Este método para representar problemas es particularmente útil cuando los problemas involucran números grandes y los estudiantes no pueden resolverlos mentalmente.

Su hijo también resolverá problemas de comparación de multiplicación y suma, y comparará este tipo de problemas para identificar las semejanzas y diferencias.

Comparación de suma	Comparación de multiplicación
Ángela tiene 14 años. Ella es 4 años mayor que Damarcus. ¿Cuántos años tiene Damarcus?	Shawn coloreó 5 páginas de un libro. Ana coloreó 4 veces ese número de páginas. ¿Cuántas páginas coloreó Ana?

Los estudiantes aprenderán que en el problema de suma están sumando 4, mientras que en el problema de multiplicación, están multiplicando por 4.

Su hijo aplicará estos conocimientos para resolver problemas de uno o más pasos usando las cuatro operaciones.

Finalmente, su hijo hallará pares de factores para números enteros y generará y analizará patrones numéricos y geométricos.

Si tiene alguna pregunta por favor comuníquese conmigo.

Atentamente,
El maestro de su niño

Properties and Algebraic Notation

compare

equation

composite number

evaluate an expression

difference

expression

A statement that two expressions are equal. It has an equal sign.

Example:
$32 + 35 = 67$
$67 = 32 + 34 + 1$
$(7 \times 8) + 1 = 57$

Describe quantities as greater than, less than, or equal to each other.

Substitute a value for a letter (or symbol) and then simplify the expression.

A number greater than 1 that has more than one factor pair. Examples of composite numbers are 10 and 18. The factor pairs of 10 are 1 and 10, 2 and 5. The factor pairs of 18 are 1 and 18, 2 and 9, 3 and 6.

A number, variable, or a combination of numbers and variables with one or more operations.

Example:
4
$6x$
$6x - 5$
$7 + 4$

The result of a subtraction.

Example:
$54 - 37 = 17$ ⟵ difference

factor pair	pattern
function	pictograph
multiple	prime number

A sequence that can be described by a rule.

A factor pair for a number is a pair of whole numbers whose product is that number.

Example:

$$5 \times 7 = 35$$

factor pair   product

A graph that uses pictures or symbols to represent data.

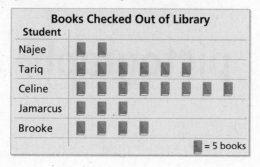

Books Checked Out of Library

Student	
Najee	📕 📕
Tariq	📕 📕 📕 📕 📕
Celine	📕 📕 📕 📕 📕 📕 📕
Jamarcus	📕 📕 📕
Brooke	📕 📕 📕 📕

📕 = 5 books

A mathematical relationship between two sets of numbers. Each number in one of the sets is paired with exactly one number in the other set. A function may be displayed in a table.

Example:
The rule for this function is *Add 2*.

Input	1	4	5	8	12
Output	3	6	7	10	14

A number greater than 1 that has 1 and itself as the only factor pair. Examples of prime numbers are 2, 7, and 13. The only factor pair of 7 is 1 and 7.

A number that is the product of a given number and any whole number.

Examples:
$4 \times 1 = 4$, so 4 is a multiple of 4.
$4 \times 2 = 8$, so 8 is a multiple of 4.

simplify an expression

sum

term

Combining like terms and performing operations until all possible terms have been combined.

The answer when adding two or more addends.

Example:

$$53 + 26 = 79$$

addend   addend   sum

A number, variable, product, or quotient in an expression or equation. Each term is separated by an operation sign (+, −).

Example:

$3n + 5$ has two terms, $3n$ and 5.

Properties and Algebraic Notation

VOCABULARY
expression
equation
simplify an expression
term

An **expression** is one or more numbers, variables, or numbers and variables with one or more operations.	An **equation** is a statement that two expressions are equal. It has an equal sign.
Examples: 4 6x 6x − 5 7 + 4	Examples: 40 + 25 = 65 (16 ÷ 4) − 3 = 1

We **simplify an expression** or equation by performing operations to combine like **terms**.

Use the Identity Property to simplify each expression.

① $n + 5n$ _____   ② $17t + t$ _____   ③ $x + 245x$ _____

④ $9e - e$ _____   ⑤ $8c + c + c$ _____   ⑥ $(5z - z) - z$ _____

Solve.

⑦ $30 \div (35 \div 7) =$ _____   ⑧ $(72 \div 9) \div 4 =$ _____

⑨ $80 \div (32 \div 8) =$ _____   ⑩ $13 - (9 - 1) =$ _____

⑪ $(600 - 400) - 10 =$ _____   ⑫ $100 - (26 - 6) =$ _____

Use properties to find the value of ▪ or a.

⑬ $49 + 17 = ▪ + 49$ ⑭ $(a \cdot 2) \cdot 3 = 4 \cdot (2 \cdot 3)$ ⑮ $▪ \cdot 6 = 6 \cdot 8$

▪ = _____ $a =$ _____   ▪ = _____

⑯ $6 \cdot (40 + a) = (6 \cdot 40) + (6 \cdot 5)$ ⑰ $(▪ \cdot 5) + (▪ \cdot 9) = 7 \cdot (5 + 9)$

$a =$ _____   ▪ = _____

⑱ $29 + 8 = ▪ + 29$ ⟶ Is ▪ = 4 + 2 or 4 · 2? _____

⑲ $a \cdot 14 = 14 \cdot 15$ ⟶ Is a = 5 · 3 or 5 + 3? _____

⑳ $60 + 10 = ▪ + 60$ ⟶ Is ▪ = 2 + 5 or 2 · 5? _____

Parentheses in Equations

VOCABULARY
evaluate an expression

Solve.

21 $9 \cdot n = 144$

$n = \underline{\hspace{1.5cm}}$

22 $s + 170 = 200$

$s = \underline{\hspace{1.5cm}}$

23 $105 \div h = 7$

$h = \underline{\hspace{1.5cm}}$

24 $9 \cdot (6 + 2) = \blacksquare \cdot 8$

$\blacksquare = \underline{\hspace{1.5cm}}$

25 $\blacksquare \cdot 6 = 96$

$\blacksquare = \underline{\hspace{1.5cm}}$

26 $(15 \div 3) \cdot (4 + 1) = v$

$v = \underline{\hspace{1.5cm}}$

27 $(12 - 5) - (12 \div 6) = \underline{\hspace{1.5cm}}$

28 $(23 + 4) \div (8 - 5) = \underline{\hspace{1.5cm}}$

29 $(24 \div 3) \cdot (12 - 7) = \underline{\hspace{1.5cm}}$

30 $(22 + 8) \div (17 - 11) = \underline{\hspace{1.5cm}}$

Substitute a Value

To **evaluate an expression** or equation, substitute a value for a letter (or symbol) and then simplify the expression by performing the operations.

Evaluate each expression.

31 $a = 4$

$19 - (a + 6)$

$\underline{\hspace{1.5cm}}$

32 $a = 10$

$(80 \div a) - 5$

$\underline{\hspace{1.5cm}}$

33 $b = 3$

$(8 \div 4) \cdot (7 - b)$

$\underline{\hspace{1.5cm}}$

34 $b = 7$

$21 \div (b - 4)$

$\underline{\hspace{1.5cm}}$

35 $b = 11$

$(b + 9) \div (7 - 2)$

$\underline{\hspace{1.5cm}}$

36 $c = 8$

$(20 - 10) + (7 + c)$

$\underline{\hspace{1.5cm}}$

37 $x = 9$

$16 \cdot (13 - x)$

$\underline{\hspace{1.5cm}}$

38 $d = 3$

$(24 \div 3) \cdot (d + 7)$

$\underline{\hspace{1.5cm}}$

39 $d = 0$

$(63 \div 7) \cdot d$

$\underline{\hspace{1.5cm}}$

✓ **Check Understanding**

Explain the steps you used to evaluate Exercise 32.

Properties and Algebraic Notation

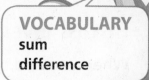

VOCABULARY
sum
difference

Discuss the = and ≠ Signs

An equation is made up of two equal quantities or expressions. An equal sign (=) is used to show that the two sides of the equation are equal.

$5 = 3 + 2$ $3 + 2 = 5$ $5 = 5$ $3 + 2 = 2 + 3$ $7 - 2 = 1 + 1 + 3$

The "is not equal to" sign (≠) shows that two quantities are not equal.

$4 \neq 3 + 2$ $5 \neq 3 - 1$ $5 \neq 4$ $3 - 2 \neq 1 + 3$ $3 + 2 \neq 1 + 1 + 2$

An equation can have one or more numbers or letters on each side of the equal sign. A **sum** or **difference** can be written on either side of the equal sign.

1 Use the = sign to write four equations. Vary how many numbers you have on each side of your equations.

_____   _____

_____   _____

2 Use the ≠ sign to write four "is not equal to" statements. Vary how many numbers you have on each side of your statements.

_____   _____

_____   _____

Write = or ≠ to make each statement true.

3 $5 + 2 + 6$ ____ $6 + 7$ **4** 80 ____ $60 - 20$

5 70 ____ $40 + 30$ **6** $18 - 4 + 11$ ____ 3

7 50 ____ $55 - (10 + 5)$ **8** $21 + 6$ ____ $31 - 4$

Discuss Inverse Operations

When you add, you put two groups together. When you subtract, you find an unknown addend or take away one group from another. Addition and subtraction are inverse operations. They undo each other.

Addends are numbers that are added to make a sum. You can find two addends for a sum by breaking apart the number.

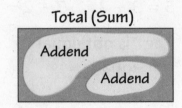

A break-apart drawing can help you find all eight related addition and subtraction equations for two addends.

Total (Sum)
81

72   9
Addend Addend

$$81 = 72 + 9 \qquad 72 + 9 = 81$$

$$81 = 9 + 72 \qquad 9 + 72 = 81$$

$$72 = 81 - 9 \qquad 81 - 9 = 72$$

$$9 = 81 - 72 \qquad 81 - 72 = 9$$

9 Which equations show the Commutative Property?

_____

_____

10 What is the total in each equation? Where is the total in a subtraction equation?

_____

_____

Solve each equation.

11 $50 = 30 + p$

$p =$ _____

12 $q + 20 = 60$

$q =$ _____

13 $90 - v = 50$

$v =$ _____

14 Write the eight related addition and subtraction equations for the break-apart drawing.

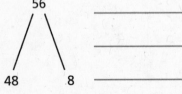

56

48   8

_____   _____

_____   _____

_____   _____

_____   _____

Write Equations to Solve Problems

A situation equation shows the structure of the information in a problem. A solution equation shows the operation that can be used to solve a problem.

Write an equation to solve the problem. Draw a model if you need to.

Show your work.

15. In a collection of 2,152 coins, 628 coins are pennies. How many coins are not pennies?

_____

_____

16. Susanna took $3,050 out of her bank account. Now she has $11,605 left in the account. How much money was in Susanna's account to start?

_____

_____

17. In the month of May, Movieland rented 563 action movies and 452 comedy movies. How many action and comedy movies in all did Movieland rent in May?

_____

_____

Practice Solving Problems

Write an equation to solve the problem. Draw a model if you need to.

18. The workers at a factory made 3,250 pink balloons in the morning. There were 5,975 pink balloons at the factory at the end of the day. How many pink balloons did the factory workers make in the afternoon?

_____

_____

Practice Solving Problems (continued)

Show your work.

19 Terrence is planning a 760-mile trip. He travels 323 miles the first two days. How many miles does Terrence have left to travel on this trip?

_____

20 There were some people at the football stadium early last Sunday, and then 5,427 more people arrived. Then there were 79,852 people at the stadium. How many people arrived early?

_____

What's the Error?

Dear Math Students,

The problem below was part of my homework assignment.

Mrs. Nason had a collection of 1,845 stamps. She bought some more stamps. Now she has 2,270 stamps. How many stamps did Mrs. Nason buy?

To solve the problem, I wrote this equation:
$s - 1,845 = 2,270$. I solved the equation and wrote $s = 4,115$.

My teacher says that my answer is not correct. Can you help me understand what I did wrong and explain how to find the correct answer?

Your friend,
Puzzled Penguin

21 Write a response to Puzzled Penguin.

_____

_____

_____

 Check Understanding

Explain the difference between a situation equation and a solution equation. Use Puzzled Penguin's homework problem to give examples of each type of equation.

Situation and Solution Equations for Addition and Subtraction

Name _____

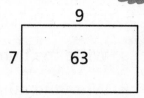

Discuss Inverse Operations

Multiplication and division are inverse operations. They undo each other.

A **factor pair** for a number is a pair of whole numbers whose product is that number. For example, a factor pair for 15 is 3 and 5. A rectangle model is a diagram that shows a factor pair and the product.

```
        9
   ┌────────────┐
 7 │     63     │
   └────────────┘
```

1 Which numbers in the rectangle model above are the factors? Where are the factors located?

_____

2 Which number is the product? Where is the product located?

_____

A rectangle model can you help you find all eight related multiplication and division equations for two factors. You can write these equations for the rectangle model above.

$$63 = 7 \times 9 \qquad\qquad 7 \times 9 = 63$$
$$63 = 9 \times 7 \qquad\qquad 9 \times 7 = 63$$
$$7 = 63 \div 9 \qquad\qquad 63 \div 9 = 7$$
$$9 = 63 \div 7 \qquad\qquad 63 \div 7 = 9$$

3 Write the eight related multiplication and division equations for the rectangle model below.

```
        12
   ┌────────────┐
 8 │     96     │
   └────────────┘
```

_____ _____

_____ _____

_____ _____

_____ _____

Write Equations to Solve Problems

Read the problem. Complete the steps to solve.

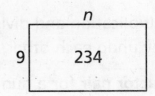

4 Brenda planted 234 trees on her farm. The farm has 9 rows of trees. How many trees are in each row?

a. Write the number of trees on the farm. _____

b. Write the number of rows of trees. _____

c. The number of trees in each row is unknown. Use the letter *n* to represent the number of trees in each row. Write a situation equation to solve the problem. _____

d. Write a solution equation. _____

e. Solve your equation. _____

Write an equation to solve the problem. Draw a model if you need to.

Show your work.

5 Evan is starting a cycling program. He will ride 315 miles each month for the next 6 months. How many miles does he plan to ride in all?

_____

6 Suki has 152 stickers to place in a sticker album. How many pages will Suki fill with stickers if she puts 8 stickers on each page?

_____

7 Al designed a wall pattern with 27 rows of 28 squares. How many squares are in the wall pattern?

_____

✔ **Check Understanding**

In Problem 6, if Suki had 248 stickers, how many pages in her album would be filled? _____

Situation and Solution Equations for Multiplication and Division

Solve for ■ or *n*.

1 $84 \div n = 6$

$n =$ _____

2 $(14 + 7) \cdot 8 = ■ \cdot 8$

$■ =$ _____

Write an equation to show the problem. Then solve. *Show your work.*

3 Miguel drove 197 miles on Monday. He drove some more miles on Tuesday. He drove 542 miles in all. How many miles did Miguel drive on Tuesday?

_____

_____

4 A theater has a seating capacity of 748 seats. If 3 performances are sold out, how many tickets are sold?

_____

_____

5 Britney is saving $996 to pay for summer camp. She wants to save the same amount of money each month for 6 months. How much money does Britney need to save each month?

_____

_____

_____

PATH to
FLUENCY

Add or subtract.

1) 242
  + 316

2) 681
  − 375

3) 2,945
  + 713

4) 5,839
  − 3,427

5) 17,649
  + 2,431

6) 48,600
  − 29,728

7) 6,739
  + 3,847

8) 5,069
  − 4,853

9) 371
  + 542

10) 574
  − 350

11) 26,366
  − 7,382

12) 34,278
  + 57,341

13) 693,317
  − 47,592

14) 242,730
  + 79,527

15) 809,411
  − 472,389

Discuss Comparison Problems

VOCABULARY
compare

To prepare for a family gathering, Sara and Ryan made soup. Sara made 2 quarts. Ryan made 6 quarts.

You can **compare** amounts, using multiplication and division.

Let *r* equal the number of quarts Ryan made.
Let *s* equal the number of quarts Sara made.

Ryan made 3 times as many quarts as Sara.

$$r = 3 \cdot s, \; r = 3s, \; \text{or} \; s = r \div 3$$

Ryan (*r*)

| 2 | 2 | 2 | 6 |

Sarah (*s*)

| 2 |

Solve.

Natasha made 12 quarts of soup. Manuel made 3 quarts.

1 Draw comparison bars to show the amount of soup each person made.

2 _____ made 4 times as many quarts as _____.

3 Write a multiplication equation that compares the amounts.

_____

4 Write a division equation that compares the amounts.

_____

5 Multiplication is the putting together of equal groups. How can this idea be used to explain why a *times as many* comparing situation is multiplication?

_____

_____

Share Solutions

Write an equation to solve each problem.
Draw a model if you need to.

Show your work.

6 There are 24 students in the science club. There are 2 times as many students in the drama club. How many students are in the drama club?

    a. Draw comparison bars to compare the numbers of students in each club.

    b. Write an equation to solve the problem.

    _____

7 There are 180 pennies in Miguel's coin collection and that is 5 times as many as the number of quarters in his coin collection. How many quarters does Miguel have?

    _____

8 Fred has 72 football cards and Scott has 6 football cards. The number of cards Fred has is how many times the number Scott has?

    _____

9 Audrey has 1,263 centimeters of fabric, and that is 3 times as much fabric as she needs to make some curtains. How many centimeters of fabric does Audrey need to make the curtains?

    _____

✓ **Check Understanding**

Draw comparison bars to represent Problem 8 and the solution.

Multiplication Comparisons

Name

Discuss Comparison Situations

In Lesson 4-4, you learned about multiplication and division comparison situations. You can also compare by using addition and subtraction. You can find *how much more* or *how much less* one amount is than another.

The amount more or less is called the difference. In some problems, the difference is not given. You have to find it. In other problems, the lesser or the greater amount is not given.

Mai has 9 apples and 12 plums.

- How many more plums than apples does Mai have?

- How many fewer apples than plums does Mai have?

Plums | 12
Apples | 9 | d

Comparison bars can help us show which amount is more. We show the difference in an oval.

Draw comparison bars for each problem. Write and solve an equation. Discuss other equations you could use.

1 A nursery has 70 rose bushes and 50 tea-tree bushes. How many fewer tea-tree bushes than rose bushes are at the nursery?

2 Dan wants to plant 30 trees. He has dug 21 holes. How many more holes does Dan need to dig?

Share Solutions

Draw comparison bars for each problem.
Write and solve an equation.

Show your models here.

3 Kyle and Maya are playing a computer game. Kyle scored 7,628 points. Maya scored 2,085 fewer points than Kyle. How many points did Maya score?

_____

_____

4 The school fair fundraiser made $632 more from baked goods than from games. The school fair made $935 from games. How much money did the school fair make from baked goods?

_____

_____

5 A college football stadium in Michigan seats 109,901 people. A college football stadium in Louisiana seats 92,542 people. How many fewer people does the stadium in Louisiana seat than the stadium in Michigan?

_____

_____

6 The soccer team drilled for 150 minutes last week. The team drilled for 30 minutes more than it scrimmaged. For how long did the team scrimmage?

_____

_____

Discuss Comparison Problems

Solve Comparison Problems

For each problem, draw a model and write *addition* or *multiplication* to identify the type of comparison. Then write and solve an equation to solve the problem.

Show your models here.

7 Nick and Liz both collect marbles. Liz has 4 times as many marbles as Nick. If Nick has 240 marbles, how many marbles does Liz have?

Type of comparison: _____

Equation and answer: _____

8 Samantha has 145 fewer songs on her portable media player than Luke has on his portable media player. If Samantha has 583 songs, how many songs does Luke have?

Type of comparison: _____

Equation and answer: _____

9 A large bookstore sold 19,813 books on Saturday and 22,964 books on Sunday. How many fewer books did the bookstore sell on Saturday than on Sunday?

Type of comparison: _____

Equation and answer: _____

_____

10 Last weekend, Mr. Morgan rode his bike 3 miles. This weekend, he rode his bike 21 miles. How many times as many miles did Mr. Morgan ride his bike this weekend as last weekend?

Type of comparison: _____

Equation and answer: _____

_____

© Houghton Mifflin Harcourt Publishing Company

Practice

Write and solve an equation to solve each problem. *Show your work.*
Draw comparison bars when needed.

11. On the last day of school, 100 more students wore
shorts than wore jeans. If 130 students wore jeans,
how many students wore shorts?

_____

12. Matthew completed a puzzle with 90 pieces. Wendy
completed a puzzle with 5 times as many pieces.
How many pieces are in Wendy's puzzle?

_____

13. There were 19,748 adults at a baseball game. There
were 5,136 fewer children at the baseball game than
adults. How many children were at the baseball game?

_____

What's the Error?

Dear Math Students,

I was asked to find the number of stamps that
Amanda has if her friend Jesse has 81 stamps and
that is 9 times as many stamps as Amanda has.

I wrote 81 × 9 = s. So, s = 729. My teacher says that my
answer is not correct. Can you explain what I did wrong?

Your friend,
Puzzled Penguin

14. Write a response to Puzzled Penguin.

_____

_____

 Check Understanding
Explain how addition comparison problems differ from
multiplication comparison problems.

Discuss Comparison Problems

Use a Pictograph

A **pictograph** is a graph that uses pictures or symbols to represent data. This pictograph shows how many books 5 students checked out of a library in one year.

Books Checked Out of Library

Student	
Najee	🔲 🔲
Tariq	🔲 🔲 🔲 🔲 🔲
Celine	🔲 🔲 🔲 🔲 🔲 🔲 🔲
Jamarcus	🔲 🔲 🔲
Brooke	🔲 🔲 🔲 🔲

🔲 = 5 books

Use the pictograph to solve.

1 Write an addition equation and a subtraction equation that compare the number of books Tariq checked out (*t*) to the number of books Jamarcus checked out (*j*).

_____

2 Write a multiplication equation and a division equation that compare the number of books Najee checked out (*n*) to the number of books Celine checked out (*c*).

_____

3 Celine checked out twice as many books as which student?

_____

4 Which student checked out 30 fewer books than Celine?

_____

5 The number of books Dawson checked out is not shown. If Jamarcus checked out 10 more books than Dawson, how many books did Dawson check out?

_____

Graphs and Comparison Problems **205**

Use a Bar Graph

The bar graph below shows the number of home runs hit by five members of a baseball team.

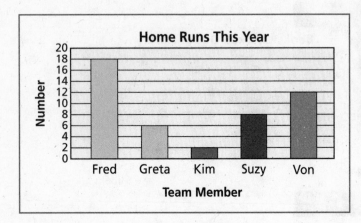

Use the bar graph to solve.

6 Write an addition equation and a subtraction equation that compare the number of home runs Suzy hit (*s*) to the number of home runs Kim hit (*k*).

_____

7 Write a multiplication equation and a division equation that compare the number of home runs Greta hit (*g*) to the number of runs Fred hit (*f*).

_____

8 How many more home runs did Von hit than Greta? _____

9 Which player hit 10 fewer home runs than Von? _____

10 This year, Fred hit 2 times as many home runs as he hit last year. How many home runs did Fred hit last year? _____

✓**Check Understanding**

Use the bar graph to solve. This year, Kim hit 8 fewer home runs than she hit last year. How many home runs did Kim hit last year?

_____

Graphs and Comparison Problems

Write an equation.

1 Nicole swims 6 times as many laps as Evan. What multiplication equation compares the laps Nicole and Evan swim?

_____

Write an equation to show the problem. Then solve.

Show your work.

2 There are 34 hats at a shop. There are 2 times as many scarves as hats at the shop. How many scarves are at the shop?

_____

3 Liam has 51 stickers. He has 3 times as many stickers as Jade. How many stickers does Jade have?

_____

4 There are 16,492 people at a car race. There are 3,271 fewer people at the race this year than last year. How many people were at the car race last year?

_____

Use the bar graph. Write an equation to solve the problem.

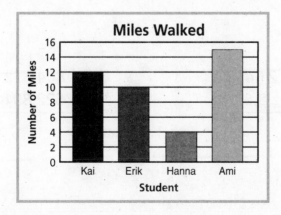

5 Kai walked how many times as many miles as Hanna?

_____

Name _____ Date _____

PATH to
FLUENCY

Add or subtract.

1
```
   214
+ 180
```

2
```
   427
-  345
```

3
```
  4,592
+ 3,667
```

4
```
  6,953
- 3,812
```

5
```
  8,931
+   658
```

6
```
  50,730
- 42,694
```

7
```
  83,314
+ 20,894
```

8
```
  9,063
- 1,842
```

9
```
   397
+ 411
```

10
```
   694
-  642
```

11
```
  76,836
-  8,565
```

12
```
  367,530
+ 246,597
```

13
```
  477,713
-  80,722
```

14
```
  21,419
+  8,639
```

15
```
  804,672
- 522,891
```

Discuss the Steps of the Problem

Sometimes you will need to work through more than one step to solve a problem. The steps can be shown in one or more equations.

Solve.

1 At Parkes Elementary School, there are 6 fourth-grade classes with 17 students in each class. On Friday, 23 fourth graders brought lunch from home and the rest of the students bought lunch in the cafeteria. How many fourth graders bought lunch in the cafeteria on Friday?

_____

2 Solve the problem again by finishing Tommy's and Lucy's methods. Then discuss how the two methods are alike and how they are different.

Tommy's Method	Lucy's Method
Write an equation for each step.	**Write an equation for the whole problem.**
Find the total number of students who are in fourth grade.	Let n = the number of students who bought lunch.
$6 \times 17 =$ _____	Students in each fourth-grade class. Students who brought lunch from home.
Subtract the number of students who brought lunch from home.	$6 \times$ _____ $-$ _____ $= n$
$102 - 23 =$ _____	_____ $= n$

3 Use an equation to solve. Discuss the steps you used.

Susan buys 16 packages of hot dogs for a barbecue. Each package contains 12 hot dogs. Hot dog buns are sold in packages of 8. How many packages of hot dog buns does Susan need to buy so she has one bun for each hot dog?

_____

Share Solutions

Use an equation to solve.   *Show your work.*

4 Admission to the theme park is $32 for each adult.
A group of 5 adults and 1 child pays $182 to enter
the theme park. How much is a child's ticket to the
theme park?

_____

5 Kenny collects CDs and DVDs. He has a total of 208 CDs.
He also has 8 shelves with 24 DVDs on each shelf.
How many more CDs does Kenny have than DVDs?

_____

6 Carla plants 14 tomato plants. Her gardening book says
that each plant should grow 12 tomatoes. She plans to
divide the tomatoes equally among herself and 7 friends.
How many tomatoes would each person get?

_____

7 Alex and his family go on a road trip. On the first
day, they drive 228 miles. On the second day, they
drive 279 miles. Their destination is 1,043 miles away.
How many miles do they have left to drive to reach
their destination?

_____

8 A public library has more than 50,000 books. There are
249 science books and 321 technology books. Mary
sorts the science and technology books on shelves
with 6 books on each shelf. How many shelves will
Mary fill with science and technology books?

_____

✓ Check Understanding

Explain what two-step problems are and how to solve them.

Name _____

Discuss the Steps

1 Mr. Stills makes bags of school supplies for the 9 students in his class. He has 108 pencils and 72 erasers. He puts the same number of pencils and the same number of erasers into each bag. How many more pencils than erasers are in each bag of school supplies?

Solve the problem by finishing Nicole's and David's methods. Discuss what is alike and what is different about the methods.

Nicole's Method

Write an equation for each step.

Divide to find the number of pencils that Mr. Stills puts in each bag of school supplies.
$$108 \div 9 = \underline{\hspace{1cm}}$$

Divide to find the number of erasers that Mr. Stills puts in each bag of school supplies.
$$72 \div 9 = \underline{\hspace{1cm}}$$

Subtract the number of erasers in each bag from the number of pencils in each bag.
$$12 - 8 = \underline{\hspace{1cm}}$$

There are _____ more pencils than erasers in each bag of school supplies.

David's Method

Write an equation for the whole problem.

Let p = how many more pencils than erasers are in each bag of school supplies.

The number of pencils in each bag of school supplies

The number of erasers in each bag of school supplies

$$\underline{\hspace{1cm}} \div 9 - \underline{\hspace{1cm}} \div 9 = p$$
$$12 - 8 = p$$
$$\underline{\hspace{1cm}} = p$$

There are _____ more pencils than erasers in each bag of school supplies.

Discuss the Steps (continued)

2 John is selling bags of popcorn for a school fundraiser. So far, John has sold 45 bags of popcorn for $5 each. His goal is to earn $300 for the school fundraiser. How many more bags of popcorn must John sell to reach his goal?

Solve the problem by writing an equation for each step.
Then solve the problem by writing one equation for the whole problem.

Write an equation for each step.

Multiply to find how much money John has earned so far selling popcorn.

_____ × $5 = $_____

Subtract to find how much money John has left to earn to reach his goal.

$300 − $_____ = $_____

Divide to find the number of bags of popcorn John must sell to reach his goal.

$75 ÷ $5 = _____

John must sell _____ more bags of popcorn to reach his goal.

Write an equation for the whole problem.

Let b = the number of bags of popcorn John must sell to reach his goal.

John's fundraiser goal amount   Amount of money John has raised so far

(_____ − _____ × $5) ÷ $5 = b

($300 − $_____) ÷ $5 = b

$_____ ÷ $5 = b

_____ = b

John must sell _____ more bags of popcorn to reach his goal.

Solve Multistep Problems

Multistep Word Problems

Use an equation to solve.

Show your work.

3 Sara bought some bags of beads. Each bag had 9 beads and cost $2. Sara used the beads to make 18 necklaces, each with 25 beads. How much money did Sara pay for the beads for all of the necklaces that she made?

4 There are 5 fourth-grade classes going on a field trip. Two of the classes have 16 students each and 3 of the classes have 17 students each. They are travelling in vans that hold 9 students each. How many vans must they have to transport all the students?

5 A movie theater has 13 screens. On weekends, each screen shows a movie 7 times in one day. On weekdays, each screen shows a movie 5 times in one day. How many more showings are there on Saturdays than on Tuesdays?

6 Justin goes to the store and buys 3 T-shirts for $14 each. He also buys 2 pairs of jeans for $23 each. He gives the cashier $100. How much change does Justin receive?

7 Terrence has 24 model cars arranged in equal rows of 6 model cars. Natalie has 18 model cars arranged in equal rows of 3 model cars. How many rows of model cars in all do they have?

What's the Error?

Dear Math Students,

My friend and I are planning a hike. We will hike from Point A to Point B, which is a distance of 28 miles. Then we will hike from Point B to Point C, which is a distance of 34 miles. We will walk 7 miles each day for 8 days. We are trying to figure out how many miles we need to walk on the ninth day to reach Point C.

I wrote and solved this equation.

$28 + 34 - 7 \times 8 = t$

$62 - 7 \times 8 = t$

$55 \times 8 = t$

$440 = t$

This answer doesn't make sense. Did I do something wrong? What do you think?

Your friend,
Puzzled Penguin

8 Write a response to Puzzled Penguin.

_____

_____

_____

_____

_____

_____

✓ Check Understanding

Describe how to solve a multistep problem.

Solve Multistep Problems

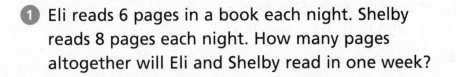

Discuss Multistep Word Problems

Use equations to solve.

Show your work.

1 Eli reads 6 pages in a book each night. Shelby reads 8 pages each night. How many pages altogether will Eli and Shelby read in one week?

_____

2 Min Soo is ordering 5 pizzas for a party. Each pizza will be cut into 8 slices. Three pizzas will have multiple toppings, and the others will be plain cheese. How many slices of plain cheese pizza is Min Soo ordering for the party?

_____

3 Jasmine and Mori each received the same number of party favor bags last month. Each bag contained 8 favors. If Jasmine and Mori received a total of 48 favors, how many party favor bags did they each receive?

_____

4 In art class, Ernesto made some fruit bowls for his mother and brother. Nine apples can be placed in each bowl. Ernesto's brother placed 18 apples in the bowls he was given, and Ernesto's mother placed 36 apples in the bowls she was given. How many fruit bowls did Ernesto make?

_____

5 On Tuesday, a bicycle shop employee replaced all of the tires on 6 bicycles. On Wednesday, all of the tires on 5 tricycles were replaced. What is the total number of tires that were replaced on those days?

_____

Solve Multistep Word Problems

Use equations to solve.

Show your work.

6 Mrs. Luong bought 9 trees for $40 each. She paid for her purchase with four $100 bills. How much change did she receive?

_____

7 The contents of Chan Hee's box weigh 37 pounds. In the box are five containers of equal weight, and a book that weighs 2 pounds. What is the weight of each container?

_____

8 A pet shop is home to 6 cats, 10 birds, 3 dogs, and 18 tropical fish. Altogether, how many legs do those pets have?

_____

9 Dan has 7 fish in his aquarium. Marilyn has 4 times as many fish in her aquarium. How many fish do Dan and Marilyn have altogether?

_____

10 Write a problem that is solved using more than one step. Then show how to solve the problem.

_____

_____

✔ **Check Understanding**

For Problem 7, suppose the contents of Chan Hee's box weigh 42 pounds. Write and solve a new equation to find the weight of each container.

_____

Practice with Multistep Problems

Write an equation to show the problem. Then solve.   *Show your work.*

1 Anika spent $128 on 3 sweaters and 1 skirt. The sweaters cost $38 each. What was the cost of the skirt?

_____

_____

2 Lily has 144 ceramic beads and 108 wooden beads. She plans to store the beads equally in 6 boxes. How many beads will be in each box?

_____

_____

Write one or more equations to show the problem. Then solve.

3 Emma has 14 rocks in her collection. Tyler has 6 times as many rocks as Emma. How many rocks do Emma and Tyler have altogether?

_____

_____

4 Joaquin is saving $250 to buy a surfboard. He saved $8 each week for 12 weeks. He wants to buy the surfboard in 7 more weeks. How much does Joaquin need to save each week?

_____

_____

Name _____   Date _____

Add or subtract.

1
$$\begin{array}{r} 60,047 \\ -\ 35,689 \\ \hline \end{array}$$

2
$$\begin{array}{r} 472 \\ -\ 364 \\ \hline \end{array}$$

3
$$\begin{array}{r} 5,682 \\ +\ 2,497 \\ \hline \end{array}$$

4
$$\begin{array}{r} 5,897 \\ -\ 4,352 \\ \hline \end{array}$$

5
$$\begin{array}{r} 89,431 \\ -\ 8,650 \\ \hline \end{array}$$

6
$$\begin{array}{r} 298 \\ +\ 311 \\ \hline \end{array}$$

7
$$\begin{array}{r} 67,538 \\ +\ 22,685 \\ \hline \end{array}$$

8
$$\begin{array}{r} 429 \\ -\ 117 \\ \hline \end{array}$$

9
$$\begin{array}{r} 409,274 \\ -\ 38,528 \\ \hline \end{array}$$

10
$$\begin{array}{r} 342 \\ +\ 342 \\ \hline \end{array}$$

11
$$\begin{array}{r} 5,630 \\ -\ 3,428 \\ \hline \end{array}$$

12
$$\begin{array}{r} 587,390 \\ +\ 136,428 \\ \hline \end{array}$$

13
$$\begin{array}{r} 984,208 \\ -\ 796,159 \\ \hline \end{array}$$

14
$$\begin{array}{r} 79,472 \\ +\ 8,927 \\ \hline \end{array}$$

15
$$\begin{array}{r} 3,219 \\ +\ 628 \\ \hline \end{array}$$

Name _____

Find Factor Pairs

A factor pair for a number is two whole numbers whose product is that number. For example, 2 and 5 is a factor pair for 10.

1 Draw arrays to show all the factor pairs for 12 on the grid below. The array for 1 and 12 is shown.

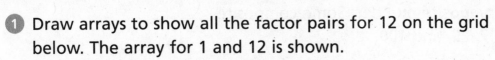

2 List all the factor pairs for 12. _____

Use the table to list all the factors pairs for each number.

3 32

1	32
2	

4 44

1	44

5 100

1	100

List all the factor pairs for each number.

6 29

_____

7 63

_____

Factors and Prime Numbers **219**

Identify Prime and Composite Numbers

VOCABULARY
prime number
composite number

A number greater than 1 that has 1 and itself as its only factor pair is a **prime number**. Some prime numbers are 2, 5, 11, and 23.

A number greater than 1 that has more than one factor pair is a **composite number**. Some composite numbers are 4, 12, 25, and 100.

The number 1 is neither prime nor composite.

8 Use counters to model the arrays for all factor pairs for 24. The array for 2 and 12 is shown below.

9 Is 24 a *prime number* or a *composite number*? Explain your answer.

_____

_____

Write whether each number is *prime* or *composite*.

10 99

_____

11 72

_____

12 31

_____

13 45

_____

14 19

_____

15 88

_____

16 67

_____

17 100

_____

18 53

_____

19 Is 2 the only even prime number? Explain.

_____

_____

Factors and Prime Numbers

Name _____

Factors and Multiples

VOCABULARY
multiple

A **multiple** of a number is a product of that number and a counting number.

20 What are the first five multiples of 4? Explain your method.

_____

_____

21 Write the first ten multiples of 8.

_____

22 Is 54 a multiple of 6? Explain how you know.

_____

_____

23 Is 6 a factor of 40? Explain how you know.

_____

24 What are the first five multiples of 9? Explain your method.

_____

_____

25 What are the factors of 63?

_____

26 Is 63 a multiple of each factor that you listed for Exercise 25? Explain how you know.

_____

_____

Practice With Factors and Multiples

Tell whether 7 is a factor of each number. Write *yes* or *no*.

27 7 _____   **28** 84 _____   **29** 93 _____   **30** 49 _____

Tell whether each number is a multiple of 9. Write *yes* or *no*.

31 27 _____   **32** 30 _____   **33** 81 _____   **34** 99 _____

Use a pattern to find the unknown multiples.

35 $3 \times 11 = 33$

   $4 \times 11 = 44$

   $5 \times 11 =$ _____

   $6 \times 11 =$ _____

   $7 \times 11 =$ _____

36 $5 \times 6 = 30$

   $6 \times 6 =$ _____

   $7 \times 6 =$ _____

   $8 \times 6 =$ _____

   $9 \times 6 =$ _____

Use the rule to complete the pattern.

37 Rule: skip count by 6

   6, _____, _____, 24, _____, 36, _____, 48, _____, 60

38 Rule: skip count by 5

   5, 10, _____, 20, 25, _____, 35, 40, _____, _____, 55, _____

39 Rule: skip count by 7

   7, 14, 21, _____, _____, _____, _____, _____, _____, _____

40 Rule: skip count by 12

   12, 24, _____, _____, _____, _____, _____, _____, _____

✓ **Check Understanding**

   Draw arrays for the factor pairs for 18. Is 18 a prime number

   or a composite number? _____

Factors and Prime Numbers

Numerical Patterns

VOCABULARY
pattern

A **pattern** is a sequence that can be described by a rule.

Use the rule to find the next three terms in the pattern.

1 22, 24, 26, 28, 30, …
Rule: add 2

_____

2 5, 10, 20, 40, …
Rule: multiply by 2

_____

3 1, 3, 9, 27, …
Rule: multiply by 3

_____

4 2, 9, 16, 23, 30, …
Rule: add 7

_____

Use the rule to find the first ten terms in the pattern.

5 First term: 9   Rule: add 5

_____

6 First term: 10   Rule: add 60

_____

Real World Applications

Solve.

7 Amy lives in the twentieth house on Elm Street. The first house on Elm Street is numbered 3. The second is 6. The third is 9. The fourth is 12. If this pattern continues, what is Amy's house number likely to be?

House	1st	2nd	3rd	4th	20th
Number	3	6	9	12	

_____

8 Theo runs 5 miles every morning. He tracks his progress on a chart to log how many miles he has run in all. How many miles will Theo write on day 100?

Day	1	2	3	4	5	100
Miles	5	10	15	20	25	

_____

Extend Patterns

9 What are the repeating terms of the pattern?

_____

10 What will be the tenth term in the pattern? _____

11 What will be the fifteenth term in the pattern? _____

Growing Patterns

12 How does each figure in the pattern at the right change from one term to the next?

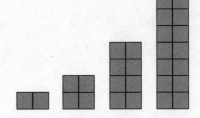

_____

_____

_____

13 Describe the number of squares in the next term in the pattern of squares.

_____

Use the pattern below to answer the questions in Exercises 14 and 15.

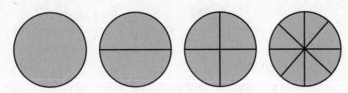

14 How does each figure in the pattern above change from one term to the next?

_____

15 How many equal parts will be in the seventh term?

_____

Analyze Patterns

Name _____

Input/Output Machines

Use the input/output machines to complete the tables.

16
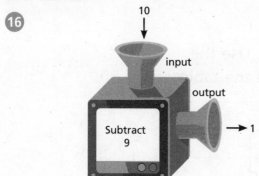

Input	Output
10	1
13	
16	
22	
25	

17
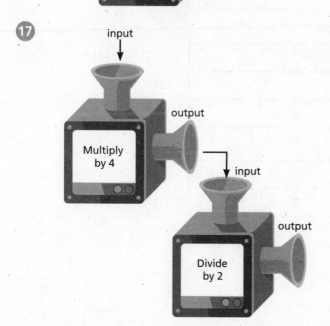

Input	Output
1	
7	
20	
4	
11	

Use Inverse Operations

Use the given operation, or its inverse operation, to find the missing values in each table.

18

Add 3				
Input	1	4			9
Output			8	15	

19

Divide by 10				
Input	20		10	50	
Output		6			10

Analyze Patterns **225**

One-Operation Functions

VOCABULARY
function

A **function** is a mathematical relationship that is shared by two sets of numbers. A rule describes the relationship. A table is a way to display a function.

For each function below, one operation is given. Use the operation, or the inverse operation, to complete the table.

20

Subtract 1					
Input	4	2		5	
Output			8		0

21

Add 5					
Input	2		3		7
Output		10		6	

22

Multiply by 11					
Input		12		9	
Output	77		110		121

Two-Operation Functions

For each function below, two operations are given. Complete the table.

23

Multiply by 3, then subtract 1					
Input	1	2	6	4	7
Output					

24

Divide by 2, then add 3					
Input	4	2	10	8	6
Output					

Analyze Patterns

Write a Rule

This table shows that the number of legs is a function of the number of dogs. Use the table to complete Exercise 25.

Number of Dogs	1	2	3	4	5	6	7	8
Number of Legs	4	8	12	16	20	24	28	32

25 Using words, write the rule of the function.

_____

_____

Make a Table

26 Write a function rule in words that includes two operations.

_____

_____

27 Write your rule from Exercise 26 in the table below. Then write five inputs. Then use the rule and write the missing outputs.

Rule: _____					
Input					
Output					

28 At a bakery, bran muffins are baked by the dozen. In the table below, write a rule to describe the relationship. Then complete the table to show the number of muffins baked for any number of dozen.

Rule: _____							
Number of Dozen							
Number of Muffins							

Functions and Equations

The function below describes the number of legs (*l*) for any number of spiders (*s*).

Number of Spiders (s)	1	2	3	4	5	6	7	8
Number of Legs (l)	8	16	24	32	40	48	56	64

29 Using the variables *s* and *l*, write an equation which shows that the number of legs (*l*) is a function of the number of spiders (*s*). _____

30 Write an equation that uses the variables *x* and *y* and shows *y* as a function of *x*.

x	0	1	2	3	4
y	1	2	3	4	5

Solve.

31 Each ticket to a school musical costs $6. Write an equation to represent the cost in dollars (*d*) for any number of tickets (*t*). _____

Jon spent $30 buying tickets. Explain how to find the number of tickets he bought. Name the number of tickets.

32 The rule for the table is $y = 3x + 2$. Use the rule to complete the table.

x	1	2	4	7	8
y					

✓ Check Understanding

Use the rule to write the first five terms in the pattern.
First term: 8; Rule: multiply by 4

Analyze Patterns

Math and Pottery

Pottery are objects that are first shaped of wet clay and then hardened by baking. Four steps are needed to make a pottery product: preparing the clay mixture, shaping the clay, decorating and glazing the product, and baking the product. Pottery includes products such as works of art, dinnerware, vases, and other household items. Some of the places you can find pottery include art studios, crafts shows, pottery stores, and many households.

Write an equation to solve.

Show your work.

1 A small pottery store has 9 same-size boxes full of pottery items. The boxes weigh 765 pounds in all. How much does each box weigh?

_____

2 Julio and Myra had a pottery stand at the annual craft fair. They sold some of their pottery at the original price of $13 each and made $780. Later in the day, they decreased the price of each item by $4 and sold 20 more items. How much money did they make in all that day?

_____

Write an equation to solve.   *Show your work.*

3 Last month, Mr. Smith bought 65 small cans of paint for his pottery shop. This month he bought 3 times as many small cans of paint. How many small cans of paint did he buy this month?

_____

4 The employees at a pottery warehouse are packing boxes of vases to be delivered by truck. They packed 824 small vases in boxes that each hold 8 vases. They also packed 296 large vases in boxes that each hold 4 vases. How many boxes did the workers pack in all?

_____

5 Last year, there were 3,875 different pottery items for sale at a large crafts show. This year, there were 1,260 fewer pottery items for sale at the crafts show. How many pottery items were for sale at the crafts show this year?

_____

Solve.

6 Isabella saw a pottery design that she liked at a crafts store. She wants to copy the design and paint it on a pot she is making. Part of the design is shown below.

a. What shape should Isabella paint next to continue the design's pattern?

_____

b. What will be the fourteenth shape in Isabella's design?

_____

Focus on Problem Solving

Write whether the number is _prime_ or _composite_.

1 91

2 41

_____

_____

3 List all factor pairs for the number.

64

_____

4 The rule for the table is $y = 2x + 1$. Use the rule to complete the table.

x	0	1	2	3	4
y					

5 Describe the next term in the pattern.

_____

_____

Name _____ Date _____

Add or subtract.

1. 24,389
    + 18,710

2. 506
    − 382

3. 5,537
    + 4,548

4. 637
    + 462

5. 43,000
    − 6,782

6. 52,896
    − 36,952

7. 11,934
    + 4,572

8. 692,375
    + 227,964

9. 353,785
    − 177,841

10. 409
    + 570

11. 4,507
    − 3,384

12. 755
    − 314

13. 430,761
    − 78,914

14. 5,396
    − 3,352

15. 8,342
    + 177

1 The number of ash trees on a tree farm is 5 times the number of pine trees. Choose one expression from each column to create an equation that compares the number of ash trees (*a*) and pine trees (*p*).

○ $a - 5$
○ $5a$
○ a
○ $a \div 5$

$=$

○ p
○ $5p$
○ $p + 5$
○ $p - 5$

2 Use the rule to find the value of *y*.

Rule: $y = 4x + 3$

value of *x*: 2

value of *y*: _____

3 Eliot sends 217 text messages each week. Write equations to find how many text messages he sends in 4 weeks and in 7 weeks.

Equations: _____

_____

Use the equations to complete the table.

Weeks	Total Text Messages
1	217
4	
7	

4 Solve for *n*.

$(16 + 12) \div (11 - 7) = n$ $n = \boxed{}$

5 There are 1,342 players in the baseball league. That is
2 times the number of players in the football league.
How many players are in the football league? Write an
equation. Then solve.

6 A school ordered 688 T-shirts in 3 sizes: small, medium,
and large. There are 296 small and 268 medium T-shirts.
How many large T-shirts were ordered? Select numbers
from the list to complete the equation. Then solve.

3	268	296	688

$$l = \boxed{} - \left(\boxed{} + \boxed{} \right)$$

$l = $ _____ large T-shirts

7 Select the factor pair for 45. Mark all that apply.

(A) 4, 11   (C) 6, 7   (E) 1, 45

(B) 3, 15   (D) 4, 12   (F) 5, 9

8 Is a multiple of the prime number 3 also a prime
number? Circle your answer.

                    Yes   No

Explain your reasoning.

9 A baker's dozen is a group or set of 13. Select the equation that shows the number of cookies (*c*) in any number of baker's dozens (*b*). Select all that apply.

(A) $c = 13b$ (C) $c = 13 + b$

(B) $c = 12b + 1$ (D) $c = b(12 + 1)$

Complete the table to show the number of cookies.

Baker's Dozens	1	3	5	7	9
Cookies					

10 Classify each number from the list as being a multiple of 2, 3, or 5. Write each number in the correct box. A number can be written in more than one box.

| 18 | 30 | 20 | 24 | 55 | 39 |

Multiple of 2	**Multiple of 3**	**Multiple of 5**

11 Use the rule to find the next 3 terms in the pattern.

Rule: multiply by 2

4, 8, 16, 32, ⬚ , ⬚ , ⬚ , ...

12 Draw the next term in the pattern.

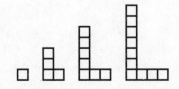

13 A team of workers is building a 942-foot trail. They plan to complete 6 feet per hour. How many hours will it take to build the trail?

Choose the equation that can be used to solve this problem. Mark all that apply.

(A) $942 \times 6 = h$ (D) $6 \times h = 942$

(B) $942 \div 6 = h$ (E) $6 = 942 \times h$

(C) $942 \div h = 6$ (F) $942 = 6 \div h$

14 Roger ships a large number of packages on Monday. Then he ships 3,820 more packages on Tuesday. Roger ships 22,540 packages in all. How many packages did he ship on Monday? Identify the type of comparison as addition or multiplication. Then write and solve an equation to solve the problem.

Type of comparison: _____

Equation: _____

Answer: _____ packages

15 For Exercises 15a–15d, select True or False for the calculation.

15a. $72 \div (6 + 2) = 9$ ○ True ○ False

15b. $(2 + 7) + (6 - 2) = 36$ ○ True ○ False

15c. $(12 + 8) \div 4 = 10 \div (5 - 3)$ ○ True ○ False

15d. $(35 - 8) \div (2 + 1) = 32$ ○ True ○ False

16 Charlotte made this pictograph to show the number of dogs attending a dog training class this week.

Dogs in Training Class

Monday	🐾 🐾 🐾
Wednesday	🐾 🐾
Friday	🐾 🐾 🐾 🐾 🐾 🐾 🐾
Saturday	🐾 🐾 🐾 🐾 🐾 🐾 🐾 🐾 🐾

🐾 = 3 dogs

Part A

How many fewer dogs were in training class on Monday than on Friday? Write and solve an equation.

Equation: _____

Answer: _____ fewer dogs

Part B

Choose the number that makes the sentence true.

Charlotte forgot to include Thursday on her graph. There were two times as many dogs at Thursday's class than at Monday's class.

There were
| 2 |
| 6 |
| 15 |
| 18 |
dogs in the training class on Thursday.

Part C

Explain how you determined the number of dogs at Thursday's class.

17 The Ruiz family bought 2 adult tickets and 4 child tickets to the fair. The adult tickets cost $8 each. The child tickets cost $3 each.

Part A
Complete the equation Zach and Alannah wrote to find the total cost of the tickets bought by the Ruiz family.

$$\left(\boxed{} \times \boxed{}\right) + \left(4 \times \boxed{}\right) = c$$

Part B
Zach's answer is $72, and Alannah's answer is $28. Who has the wrong answer? Explain what error he or she made.

18 A store has 4 bins of planet posters with 23 posters in each bin. It has 3 bins of planet calendars with 26 calendars in each bin. Yesterday, 72 calendars were sold. How many planet posters and calendars are left in all? Explain how you found your answer and how you know if your answer is reasonable.

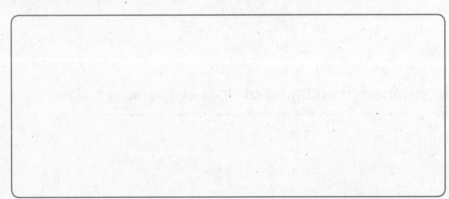

Find Their Ages

Tricia, Molly, and Becky are cousins. At a family reunion, their Aunt Sasha makes it a game for the other relatives to find the age of each cousin. Aunt Sasha tells the relatives that Becky is 2 years older than Molly. She says that Tricia's age is 3 times Molly's age right now.

1 Write an equation relating Becky's age to Molly's age.

_____

2 Write an equation relating Tricia's age to Molly's age.

_____

3 If Molly is 3, how old is Becky? Show your work.

_____

_____

4 How old is Tricia? Show your work.

_____

_____

5 Write an equation that relates Tricia's age to Becky's age. Show that your equation is true.

_____

_____

_____

_____

James, Ben, and David are cousins who are also at the family reunion. James is 12 years old, Ben is 16 years old, and David is 18 years old. The cousins decide to play a game for the other relatives to find the ages of their uncles.

6 The cousins said that Uncle Reggie is twice as many years old as James' and Ben's ages together. Use one or more equations to find out how old Uncle Reggie is. Show your work.

_____

_____

7 Then the cousins said that Uncle Tony is 4 years younger than 3 times David's age. Use one or more equations to find out how old Uncle Tony is. Show your work.

_____

_____

8 The cousins also said that Uncle Ed is half as old as all of their ages combined. Use one or more equations to find out how old Uncle Ed is. Show your work.

_____

_____

9 Write and solve an equation relating your age to the age of someone in your family. Use at least one variable. Explain how you wrote the equation.

_____

_____

_____

Examples of Metric Units

Length

1 kilometer (km)	1 hectometer (hm)	1 dekameter (dam)	1 meter (m)
about the distance you could walk in 12 minutes 1 km = 1,000 m	about the length of a football field 1 hm = 100 m	about the length of a school bus 1 dam = 10 m	about the distance from the floor to the doorknob
	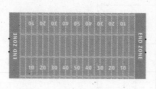		

1 decimeter (dm)	1 centimeter (cm)	1 millimeter (mm)
about the length of a new crayon 10 dm = 1 m	about the width of your finger 100 cm = 1 m	about the thickness of a dime 1,000 mm = 1 m

Metric Units

Examples of Metric Units

Liquid Volume

1 kiloliter (kL)	1 liter (L)	1 milliliter (mL)

This cube holds 1 kiloliter of liquid.

1 kL = 1,000 L

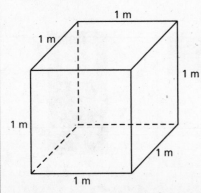

This cube holds 1 liter of liquid.

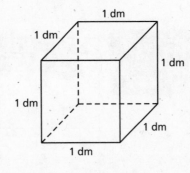

This cube holds 1 milliliter of liquid.

1,000 mL = 1 L

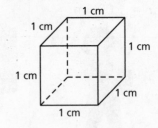

Mass

1 kilogram (kg)	1 gram (g)	1 milligram (mg)

The mass of 5 bananas is about 1 kilogram.

1 kg = 1,000 g

The mass of a paper clip is about 1 gram.

The mass of a pinch of salt is about 1 milligram.

1,000 mg = 1 g

Examples of Customary Units

Length

1 inch (in.)	1 foot (ft)	1 yard (yd)	1 mile (mi)
The distance across a quarter is about 1 inch.	The length of your math book is about 1 foot. 1 ft = 12 in.	The length of a guitar is about 1 yard. 1 yd = 3 ft	You can walk 1 mile in about 20 minutes. 1 mi = 5,280 ft = 1,760 yd

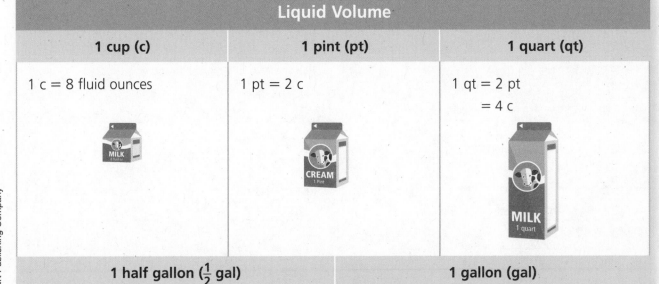

Liquid Volume

1 cup (c)	1 pint (pt)	1 quart (qt)
1 c = 8 fluid ounces	1 pt = 2 c	1 qt = 2 pt = 4 c

1 half gallon ($\frac{1}{2}$ gal)	1 gallon (gal)
$\frac{1}{2}$ gal = 2 qt	1 gal = 4 qt

Customary Units

Examples of Customary Units		
Weight		
1 ounce (oz)	**1 pound (lb)**	**1 ton (T)**
A slice of bread weighs about 1 ounce.	A package of butter weighs 1 pound. 1 lb = 16 oz	A small car weighs about 1 ton. 1 T = 2,000 lb

Table of Measures

Metric	Customary

Length/Area

1,000 millimeters (mm) = 1 meter (m)	1 foot (ft) = 12 inches (in.)
100 centimeters (cm) = 1 meter	1 yard (yd) = 36 inches
10 decimeters (dm) = 1 meter	1 yard = 3 feet
1 dekameter (dam) = 10 meters	1 mile (mi) = 5,280 feet
1 hectometer (hm) = 100 meters	1 mile = 1,760 yards
1 kilometer (km) = 1,000 meters	

Liquid Volume

1,000 milliliters (mL) = 1 liter (L)	6 teaspoons (tsp) = 1 fluid ounce (fl oz)
100 centiliters (cL) = 1 liter	2 tablespoons (tbsp) = 1 fluid ounce
10 deciliters (dL) = 1 liter	1 cup (c) = 8 fluid ounces
1 dekaliter (daL) = 10 liters	1 pint (pt) = 2 cups
1 hectoliter (hL) = 100 liters	1 quart (qt) = 2 pints
1 kiloliter (kL) = 1,000 liters	1 gallon (gal) = 4 quarts

Mass / Weight

Mass	Weight
1,000 milligrams (mg) = 1 gram (g)	1 pound (lb) = 16 ounces
100 centigrams (cg) = 1 gram	1 ton (T) = 2,000 pounds
10 decigrams (dg) = 1 gram	
1 dekagram (dag) = 10 grams	
1 hectogram (hg) = 100 grams	
1 kilogram (kg) = 1,000 grams	
1 metric ton = 1,000 kilograms	

Table of Units of Time

Time

1 minute (min) = 60 seconds (sec)	1 year = 365 days
1 hour (hr) = 60 minutes	1 leap year = 366 days
1 day = 24 hours	1 decade = 10 years
1 week (wk) = 7 days	1 century = 100 years
1 month is about 30 days	1 millennium = 1,000 years
1 year (yr) = 12 months (mo) or about 52 weeks	

Table of Formulas

Perimeter

Polygon
P = sum of the lengths of the sides

Rectangle
$P = 2(l + w)$ or $P = 2l + 2w$

Square
$P = 4s$

Area

Rectangle
$A = lw$ or $A = bh$

Square
$A = s \cdot s$

Properties of Operations

Associative Property of Addition

$(a + b) + c = a + (b + c)$	$(2 + 5) + 3 = 2 + (5 + 3)$

Commutative Property of Addition

$a + b = b + a$	$4 + 6 = 6 + 4$

Addition Identity Property of 0

$a + 0 = 0 + a = a$	$3 + 0 = 0 + 3 = 3$

Associative Property of Multiplication

$(a \cdot b) \cdot c = a \cdot (b \cdot c)$	$(3 \cdot 5) \cdot 7 = 3 \cdot (5 \cdot 7)$

Commutative Property of Multiplication

$a \cdot b = b \cdot a$	$6 \cdot 3 = 3 \cdot 6$

Multiplicative Identity Property of 1

$a \cdot 1 = 1 \cdot a = a$	$8 \cdot 1 = 1 \cdot 8 = 8$

Distributive Property of Multiplication over Addition

$a \cdot (b + c) = (a \cdot b) + (a \cdot c)$	$2 \cdot (4 + 3) = (2 \cdot 4) + (2 \cdot 3)$

Problem Types

Addition and Subtraction Problem Types

	Result Unknown	Change Unknown	Start Unknown
Add to	A glass contained $\frac{3}{4}$ cup of orange juice. Then $\frac{1}{4}$ cup of pineapple juice was added. How much juice is in the glass now? *Situation and solution equation:* [1] $\frac{3}{4} + \frac{1}{4} = c$	A glass contained $\frac{3}{4}$ cup of orange juice. Then some pineapple juice was added. Now the glass contains 1 cup of juice. How much pineapple juice was added? *Situation equation:* $\frac{3}{4} + c = 1$ *Solution equation:* $c = 1 - \frac{3}{4}$	A glass contained some orange juice. Then $\frac{1}{4}$ cup of pineapple juice was added. Now the glass contains 1 cup of juice. How much orange juice was in the glass to start? *Situation equation:* $c + \frac{1}{4} = 1$ *Solution equation:* $c = 1 - \frac{1}{4}$
Take from	Micah had a ribbon $\frac{5}{6}$ yard long. He cut off a piece $\frac{1}{6}$ yard long. What is the length of the ribbon that is left? *Situation and solution equation:* $\frac{5}{6} - \frac{1}{6} = r$	Micah had a ribbon $\frac{5}{6}$ yard long. He cut off a piece. Now the ribbon is $\frac{4}{6}$ yard long. What is the length of the ribbon he cut off? *Situation equation:* $\frac{5}{6} - r = \frac{4}{6}$ *Solution equation:* $r = \frac{5}{6} - \frac{4}{6}$	Micah had a ribbon. He cut off a piece $\frac{1}{6}$ yard long. Now the ribbon is $\frac{4}{6}$ yard long. What was the length of the ribbon he started with? *Situation equation:* $r - \frac{1}{6} = \frac{4}{6}$ *Solution equation:* $r = \frac{4}{6} + \frac{1}{6}$

[1]A situation equation represents the structure (action) in the problem situation. A solution equation shows the operation used to find the answer.

Addition and Subtraction Problem Types (continued)

	Total Unknown	Addend Unknown	Other Addend Unknown
Put Together/ Take Apart	A baker combines $1\frac{2}{3}$ cups of white flour and $\frac{2}{3}$ cup of wheat flour. How much flour is this altogether? *Math drawing:*[1] *Situation and solution equation:* $1\frac{2}{3} + \frac{2}{3} = f$	Of the $2\frac{1}{3}$ cups of flour a baker uses, $1\frac{2}{3}$ cups are white flour. The rest is wheat flour. How much wheat flour does the baker use? *Math drawing:*  *Situation equation:* $2\frac{1}{3} = 1\frac{2}{3} + f$ *Solution equation:* $f = 2\frac{1}{3} - 1\frac{2}{3}$	A baker uses $2\frac{1}{3}$ cups of flour. Some is white flour and $\frac{2}{3}$ cup is wheat flour. How much white flour does the baker use? *Math drawing:* $2\frac{1}{3}$ $f \qquad \frac{2}{3}$ *Situation equation:* $2\frac{1}{3} = f + \frac{2}{3}$ *Solution equation:* $f = 2\frac{1}{3} - \frac{2}{3}$

Both Addends Unknown is a productive extension of this basic situation, especially for finding two fractions with a sum of 1. Such take apart situations can be used to show all the decompositions of a given number. The associated equations, which have the total on the left of the equal sign, help students understand that the = sign does not always mean *makes* or *results in* but always does mean *is the same number as*.

Both Addends Unknown

A baker is making different kinds of bread using only the $\frac{1}{4}$ cup measure. What different mixtures can be made with white flour and wheat flour to total 1 cup?

Math drawing:

Situation equation:

$1 = \square + \square$

[1]These math drawings are called math mountains in Grades 1–3 and break apart drawings in Grades 4 and 5.

Problem Types

Addition and Subtraction Problem Types (continued)

	Difference Unknown	Greater Unknown	Smaller Unknown
Additive Comparison[1]	At a zoo, the female rhino weighs $1\frac{3}{5}$ tons. The male rhino weighs $2\frac{2}{5}$ tons. How much more does the male rhino weigh than the female rhino? At a zoo, the female rhino weighs $1\frac{3}{5}$ tons. The male rhino weighs $2\frac{2}{5}$ tons. How much less does the female rhino weigh than the male rhino? *Math drawing:* $2\frac{2}{5}$ $1\frac{3}{5}$ d *Situation equation:* $1\frac{3}{5} + d = 2\frac{2}{5}$ or $d = 2\frac{2}{5} - 1\frac{3}{5}$ *Solution equation:* $d = 2\frac{2}{5} - 1\frac{3}{5}$	**Leading Language** At a zoo, the female rhino weighs $1\frac{3}{5}$ tons. The male rhino weighs $\frac{4}{5}$ ton more than the female rhino. How much does the male rhino weigh? **Misleading Language** At a zoo, the female rhino weighs $1\frac{3}{5}$ tons. The female rhino weighs $\frac{4}{5}$ ton less than the male rhino. How much does the male rhino weigh? *Math drawing:* m $1\frac{3}{5}$ $\frac{4}{5}$ *Situation and solution equation:* $1\frac{3}{5} + \frac{4}{5} = m$	**Leading Language** At a zoo, the male rhino weighs $2\frac{2}{5}$ tons. The female rhino weighs $\frac{4}{5}$ ton less than the male rhino. How much does the female rhino weigh? **Misleading Language** At a zoo, the male rhino weighs $2\frac{2}{5}$ tons. The male rhino weighs $\frac{4}{5}$ ton more than the female rhino. How much does the female rhino weigh? *Math drawing:* $2\frac{2}{5}$ f $\frac{4}{5}$ *Situation equation:* $f + \frac{4}{5} = 2\frac{2}{5}$ or $f = 2\frac{2}{5} - \frac{4}{5}$ *Solution equation:* $f = 2\frac{2}{5} - \frac{4}{5}$

[1]A comparison sentence can always be said in two ways. One way uses *more*, and the other uses *fewer* or *less*. Misleading language suggests the wrong operation. For example, it says *the female rhino weighs $\frac{4}{5}$ ton less than the male*, but you have to add $\frac{4}{5}$ ton to the female's weight to get the male's weight.

Multiplication and Division Problem Types

	Product Unknown	Group Size Unknown	Number of Groups Unknown
Equal Groups	A teacher bought 10 boxes of pencils. There are 20 pencils in each box. How many pencils did the teacher buy? *Situation and solution equation:* $p = 10 \cdot 20$	A teacher bought 10 boxes of pencils. She bought 200 pencils in all. How many pencils are in each box? *Situation equation:* $10 \cdot n = 200$ *Solution equation:* $n = 200 \div 10$	A teacher bought boxes of 20 pencils. She bought 200 pencils in all. How many boxes of pencils did she buy? *Situation equation:* $b \cdot 20 = 200$ *Solution equation:* $b = 200 \div 20$

	Product Unknown	Factor Unknown	Factor Unknown
Arrays[1]	An auditorium has 60 rows with 30 seats in each row. How many seats are in the auditorium? *Math drawing:* 30 60 s *Situation and solution equation:* $s = 60 \cdot 30$	An auditorium has 60 rows with the same number of seats in each row. There are 1,800 seats in all. How many seats are in each row? *Math drawing:* n 60 1,800 *Situation equation:* $60 \cdot n = 1,800$ *Solution equation:* $n = 1,800 \div 60$	The 1,800 seats in an auditorium are arranged in rows of 30. How many rows of seats are there? *Math drawing:* 30 r 1,800 *Situation equation:* $r \cdot 30 = 1,800$ *Solution equation:* $r = 1,800 \div 30$

[1]We use rectangle models for both array and area problems in Grades 4 and 5 because the numbers in the problems are too large to represent with arrays.

Multiplication and Division Problem Types (continued)

	Product Unknown	Factor Unknown	Factor Unknown
Area	Sophie's backyard is 80 feet long and 40 feet wide. What is the area of Sophie's backyard? Math drawing: 80 40 $\boxed{A}$ Situation and solution equation: $A = 80 \cdot 40$	Sophie's backyard has an area of 3,200 square feet. The length of the yard is 80 feet. What is the width of the yard? Math drawing: 80 w $\boxed{3{,}200}$ Situation equation: $80 \cdot w = 3{,}200$ Solution equation: $w = 3{,}200 \div 80$	Sophie's backyard has an area of 3,200 square feet. The width of the yard is 40 feet. What is the length of the yard? Math drawing: l 40 $\boxed{3{,}200}$ Situation equation: $l \cdot 40 = 3{,}200$ Solution equation: $l = 3{,}200 \div 40$
Multiplicative Comparison	**Multiplier 1: Larger Unknown** Sam has 4 times as many marbles as Brady has. Brady has 70 marbles. How many marbles does Sam have? Math drawing: s	70	70	70	70 | b	70 | $b = s \div 4$ and $s = 4 \cdot b$ Situation and solution equation: $s = 4 \cdot 70$	**Multiplier 1: Smaller Unknown** Sam has 4 times as many marbles as Brady has. Sam has 280 marbles. How many marbles does Brady have? Math drawing: 280 s b $b = s \div 4$ and $s = 4 \cdot b$ Situation equation: $4 \cdot b = 280$ Situation and solution equation: $b = 280 \div 4$	**Multiplier 1: Unknown** Sam has 280 marbles. Brady has 70 marbles. The number of marbles Sam has is how many times the number Brady has? Math drawing: 280 s	70	70	70	70 | b	70 | $m \cdot b = s$ Situation equation: $m \cdot 70 = 280$ Solution equation: $m = 280 \div 70$

MathWord **Power**

Word Review

Work with a partner. Choose a word from the current unit or a review word from a previous unit. Use the word to complete one of the activities listed on the right. Then ask your partner if they have any edits to your work or questions about what you described. Repeat, having your partner choose a word.

Activities

- Give the meaning in words or gestures.
- Use the word in a sentence.
- Give another word that is related to the word in some way and explain the relationship.

Crossword Puzzle

Create a crossword puzzle similar to the example below. Use vocabulary words from the unit. You can add other related words, too. Challenge your partner to solve the puzzle.

Across

2. The answer to an addition problem
4. _____ and subtraction are inverse operations.
5. To put amounts together
6. When you trade 10 ones for 1 ten, you _____.

Down

1. The number to be divided in a division problem
2. The operation that you can use to find out how much more one number is than another.
3. A fraction with a numerator of 1 is a _____ fraction.

Vocabulary Activities

Word Wall

With your teacher's permission, start a word wall in your classroom. As you work through each lesson, put the math vocabulary words on index cards and place them on the word wall. You can work with a partner or a small group choosing a word and giving the definition.

Word Web

Make a word web for a word or words you do not understand in a unit. Fill in the web with words or phrases that are related to the vocabulary word.

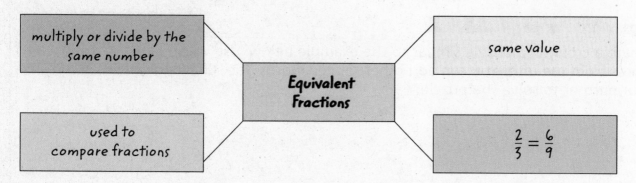

multiply or divide by the same number		same value
	Equivalent Fractions	
used to compare fractions		$\frac{2}{3} = \frac{6}{9}$

Alphabet Challenge

Take an alphabet challenge. Choose 3 letters from the alphabet. Think of three vocabulary words for each letter. Then write the definition or draw an example for each word.

A	E	L
addition	equation	liter
Associative Property	expanded form	line
area	estimate	line plot

Concentration

Write the vocabulary words and related words from a unit on index cards. Write the definitions on a different set of index cards. Choose 3 to 6 pairs of vocabulary words and definitions. Mix up the set of pairs. Then place the cards facedown on a table. Take turns turning over two cards. If one card is a word and one card is a definition that matches the word, take the pair. Continue until each word has been matched with its definition.

area

The number of square units that cover a figure.

Math Journal

As you learn new words, write them in your Math Journal. Write the definition of the word and include a sketch or an example. As you learn new information about the word, add notes to your definition.

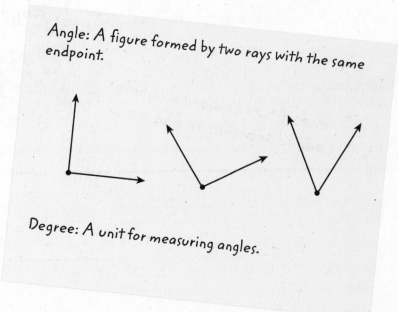

Angle: A figure formed by two rays with the same endpoint.

Degree: A unit for measuring angles.

Vocabulary Activities

What's the Word?

Work together to make a poster or bulletin board display of the words in a unit. Write definitions on a set of index cards. Mix up the cards. Work with a partner, choosing a definition from the index cards. Have your partner point to the word on the poster and name the matching math vocabulary word. Switch roles and try the activity again.

array

place value

addend

inverse operations

expanded form

word form

standard form

digit

one of two or more numbers added together to find a sum

A

acute angle

An angle smaller than a right angle.

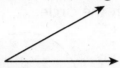

acute triangle

A triangle with three acute angles.

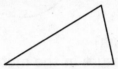

addend

One of two or more numbers added together to find a sum.

Example:

$$7 + 8 = 15$$

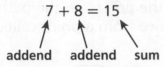

addend   addend   sum

adjacent sides

Two sides that meet at a point.

Example:

Sides *a* and *b* are adjacent.

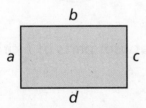

Algebraic Notation Method*

A strategy based on the Distributive Property in which a factor is decomposed to create simpler algebraic expressions, and the Distributive Property is applied.

Example:

$$9 \cdot 28 = 9 \cdot (20 + 8)$$
$$= (9 \cdot 20) + (9 \cdot 8)$$
$$= 180 + 72$$
$$= 252$$

analog clock

A clock with a face and hands.

angle

A figure formed by two rays with the same endpoint.

area

The number of square units that cover a figure.

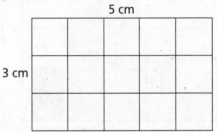

5 cm

3 cm

array

An arrangement of objects, symbols, or numbers in rows and columns.

Associative Property of Addition

Grouping the addends in different ways does not change the sum.

Example:

$$3 + (5 + 7) = 15$$
$$(3 + 5) + 7 = 15$$

*A classroom research-based term developed for *Math Expressions*

Glossary

Associative Property of Multiplication

Grouping the factors in different ways does not change the product.

Example:

$3 \times (5 \times 7) = 105$

$(3 \times 5) \times 7 = 105$

B

bar graph

A graph that uses bars to show data. The bars may be vertical or horizontal.

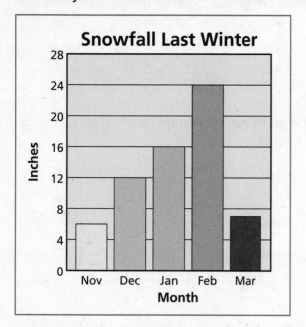

break-apart drawing*

A diagram that shows two addends and the sum.

C

center

The point that is the same distance from every point on the circle.

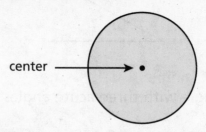

centimeter (cm)

A unit of measure in the metric system that equals one hundredth of a meter.

100 cm = 1 m

circle

A plane figure that forms a closed path so that all the points on the path are the same distance from a point called the center.

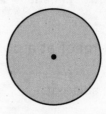

circle graph

A graph that uses parts of a circle to show data.

*A classroom research-based term developed for *Math Expressions*

column
A part of a table or array that contains items arranged vertically.

• • • •
• • • •
• • • •
• • • •

common denominator
A common multiple of two or more denominators.

Example:
A common denominator of $\frac{1}{2}$ and $\frac{1}{3}$ is 6 because 6 is a multiple of 2 and 3.

Commutative Property of Addition
Changing the order of addends does not change the sum.

Example: 3 + 8 = 11
        8 + 3 = 11

Commutative Property of Multiplication
Changing the order of factors does not change the product.

Example: 3 × 8 = 24
        8 × 3 = 24

compare
Describe quantities as greater than, less than, or equal to each other.

comparison bars*
Bars that represent the larger amount and smaller amount in a comparison situation.

For addition and subtraction:

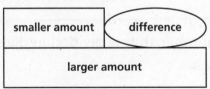

For multiplication and division:

smaller amount	smaller amount	smaller amount	larger amount

smaller amount		

comparison situation*
A situation in which two amounts are compared by addition or by multiplication. An *addition comparison situation* compares by asking or telling how much more (how much less) one amount is than another. A *multiplication comparison situation* compares by asking or telling how many times as many one amount is as another. The multiplication comparison may also be made using fraction language. For example, you can say, "Sally has one fourth as much as Tom has," instead of saying "Tom has 4 times as much as Sally has."

compatible numbers
Numbers that are easy to compute with mentally.

Example:

$9)\overline{5,841}$ Some compatible numbers for the divisor and dividend are 9 and 5,400, and 9 and 6,300.

composite number
A number greater than 1 that has more than one factor pair. Examples of composite numbers are 10 and 18. The factor pairs of 10 are 1 and 10, 2 and 5. The factor pairs of 18 are 1 and 18, 2 and 9, 3 and 6.

congruent
Figures that are the same size and shape.

cup (c)
A unit of liquid volume in the U.S. customary system that equals 8 fluid ounces.

D

data
A collection of information.

*A classroom research-based term developed for *Math Expressions*

Glossary

decimal number

A representation of a number using the numerals 0 to 9, in which each digit has a value 10 times the digit to its right. A dot or **decimal point** separates the whole-number part of the number on the left from the fractional part on the right.

Examples:
1.23 and 0.3

decimal point

A symbol used to separate dollars and cents in money amounts or to separate ones and tenths in decimal numbers.

Examples:

$8.59   1.2

decimal point

decimeter (dm)

A unit of measure in the metric system that equals one tenth of a meter.
10 dm = 1 m

degree (°)

A unit for measuring angles.

denominator

The number below the bar in a fraction. It shows the total number of equal parts in the whole.

Example:

$\frac{3}{4}$ ← denominator

diagonal of a quadrilateral

A line segment that connects two opposite corners (vertices).

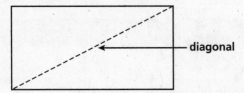

diagonal

difference

The result of a subtraction.

Example:
54 − 37 = 17 ← difference

digit

Any of the symbols 0, 1, 2, 3, 4, 5, 6, 7, 8, or 9.

digital clock

A clock that shows the hour and minutes with numbers.

Digit-by-Digit Method*

A method used to solve a division problem.

Put in only one digit at a time.

$$
\begin{array}{r}
5 \\
7\overline{)3{,}822} \\
-35 \\
\hline
32
\end{array}
\qquad
\begin{array}{r}
54 \\
7\overline{)3{,}822} \\
-35 \\
\hline
32 \\
-28 \\
\hline
42
\end{array}
\qquad
\begin{array}{r}
546 \\
7\overline{)3{,}822} \\
-35 \\
\hline
32 \\
-28 \\
\hline
42 \\
-42
\end{array}
$$

Distributive Property

Multiplying a sum by a number, or multiplying each addend by the number and adding the products; the result is the same.

Example:
3 × (2 + 4) = (3 × 2) + (3 × 4)
  3 × 6   =   6   +   12
    18   =   18

dividend

The number that is divided in division.

Example:

$$
\begin{array}{r}
7 \\
9\overline{)63}
\end{array}
$$

63 is the dividend.

divisible

A number is divisible by another number if the quotient is a whole number with a remainder of 0.

*A classroom research-based term developed for *Math Expressions*

divisor

The number you divide by in division.

Example:

$$9\overline{)63}^{7}$$

9 is the divisor.

dot array

An arrangement of dots in rows and columns.

E

elapsed time

The time that passes between the beginning and the end of an activity.

endpoint

The point at either end of a line segment or the beginning point of a ray.

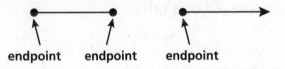

endpoint   endpoint   endpoint

equation

A statement that two expressions are equal. It has an equal sign.

Examples:

$32 + 35 = 67$

$67 = 32 + 34 + 1$

$(7 \times 8) + 1 = 57$

equilateral triangle

A triangle with three sides of equal length.

equivalent fractions

Two or more fractions that represent the same number.

Example:

$\frac{2}{4}$ and $\frac{4}{8}$ are equivalent because they both represent one half.

estimate

A number close to an exact amount or to find about how many or how much.

evaluate an expression

Substitute a value for a letter (or symbol) and then simplify the expression.

expanded form

A way of writing a number that shows the value of each of its digits.

Example:

Expanded form of 835:

$800 + 30 + 5$

8 hundreds + 3 tens + 5 ones

Expanded Notation Method*

A method used to solve multiplication and division problems.

Examples:

43×67

$$
\begin{aligned}
67 &= 60 + 7 \\
\times 43 &= 40 + 3 \\
\hline
40 \times 60 &= 2400 \\
40 \times 7 &= 280 \\
3 \times 60 &= 180 \\
3 \times 7 &= +21 \\
\hline
&2{,}881
\end{aligned}
$$

$3{,}822 \div 7$

$$
\begin{array}{r}
6 \\
40\overline{)546} \\
500 \\
7\overline{)3{,}822} \\
-3\,500 \\
\hline
322 \\
-280 \\
\hline
42 \\
-42 \\
\hline
0
\end{array}
$$

*A classroom research-based term developed for *Math Expressions*

Glossary

expression
A number, variable, or a combination of numbers and variables with one or more operations.

Examples:

4

$6x$

$6x - 5$

$7 + 4$

factor
One of two or more numbers multiplied to find a product.

Example:

$$4 \times 5 = 20$$

factor   factor   product

factor pair
A factor pair for a number is a pair of whole numbers whose product is that number.

Example:

$$5 \times 7 = 35$$

factor pair   product

fluid ounce (fl oz)
A unit of liquid volume in the U.S. customary system.

8 fluid ounces = 1 cup

foot (ft)
A U.S. customary unit of length equal to 12 inches.

formula
An equation with letters or symbols that describes a rule.

The formula for the area of a rectangle is:

$A = l \times w$

where A is the area, l is the length, and w is the width.

fraction
A number that is the sum of unit fractions, each an equal part of a set or part of a whole.

Examples:

$$\frac{3}{4} = \frac{1}{4} + \frac{1}{4} + \frac{1}{4}$$

$$\frac{5}{4} = \frac{1}{4} + \frac{1}{4} + \frac{1}{4} + \frac{1}{4} + \frac{1}{4}$$

function
A mathematical relationship between two sets of numbers. Each number in one of the sets is paired with exactly one number in the other set. A function may be displayed in a table.

Example:
The rule for this function is *Add 2*.

Input	1	4	5	8	12
Output	3	6	7	10	14

gallon (gal)
A unit of liquid volume in the U.S. customary system that equals 4 quarts.

gram (g)
The basic unit of mass in the metric system.

greater than (>)
A symbol used to compare two numbers. The greater number is given first below.

Example:
33 > 17
33 is greater than 17.

group
To combine numbers to form new tens, hundreds, thousands, and so on.

H

hundredth
A unit fraction representing one of one hundred parts, written as 0.01 or $\frac{1}{100}$.

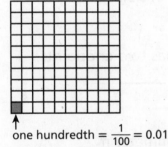

7.634
↑
hundredth

one hundredth = $\frac{1}{100}$ = 0.01

I

Identity Property of Multiplication
The product of 1 and any number equals that number.

Example:
$10 \times 1 = 10$

inch
A U.S. customary unit of length.

1 inch

inequality
A statement that two expressions are not equal.

Examples:
2 < 5
4 + 5 > 12 − 8

intersecting lines
Lines that meet at a point.

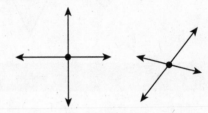

inverse operations
Opposite or reverse operations that undo each other. Addition and subtraction are inverse operations. Multiplication and division are inverse operations.

Examples:
4 + 6 = 10 so, 10 − 6 = 4 and 10 − 4 = 6.
3 × 9 = 27 so, 27 ÷ 9 = 3 and 27 ÷ 3 = 9.

isosceles triangle
A triangle with at least two sides of equal length.

K

kilogram (kg)
A unit of mass in the metric system that equals one thousand grams.

1 kg = 1,000 g

kiloliter (kL)
A unit of liquid volume in the metric system that equals one thousand liters.

1 kL = 1,000 L

Glossary

kilometer (km)

A unit of length in the metric system that equals 1,000 meters.

1 km = 1,000 m

kite

A quadrilateral with two pairs of equal adjacent sides.

L

least common denominator

The least common multiple of two or more denominators.

Example:

The least common denominator of $\frac{1}{2}$ and $\frac{1}{3}$ is 6 because 6 is the smallest multiple of 2 and 3.

length

The measure of a line segment or the distance across the longer side of a rectangle.

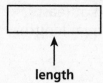

length

less than (<)

A symbol used to compare two numbers. The smaller number is given first below.

Example:

54 < 78

54 is less than 78.

line

A straight path that goes on forever in opposite directions.

Example:

line AB

line of symmetry

A line on which a figure can be folded so that the two halves match exactly.

line of symmetry

line plot

A diagram that shows the frequency of data on a number line. Also called a dot plot.

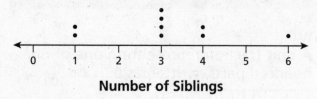

Number of Siblings

line segment

Part of a line that has two endpoints.

line symmetry

A figure has line symmetry if it can be folded along a line to create two halves that match exactly.

liquid volume

A measure of the space a liquid occupies.

liter (L)

The basic unit of liquid volume in the metric system.

1 liter = 1,000 milliliters

M

mass
The measure of the amount of matter in an object.

meter (m)
The basic unit of length in the metric system.

metric system
A base ten system of measurement.

mile (mi)
A U.S. customary unit of length equal to 5,280 feet.

milligram (mg)
A unit of mass in the metric system.
1,000 mg = 1g

milliliter (mL)
A unit of liquid volume in the metric system.
1,000 mL = 1 L

millimeter (mm)
A unit of length in the metric system.
1,000 mm = 1 m

mixed number
A number that can be represented by a whole number and a fraction.
Example:
$4\frac{1}{2} = 4 + \frac{1}{2}$

multiple
A number that is the product of a given number and any whole number.
Examples:
4 × 1 = 4, so 4 is a multiple of 4.
4 × 2 = 8, so 8 is a multiple of 4.

N

number line
A line that extends, without end, in each direction and shows numbers as a series of points. The location of each number is shown by its distance from 0.

numerator
The number above the bar in a fraction. It shows the number of equal parts.
Example:

$\frac{3}{4}$ ⟵ **numerator** $\frac{3}{4} = \frac{1}{4} + \frac{1}{4} + \frac{1}{4}$

O

obtuse angle
An angle greater than a right angle and less than a straight angle.

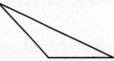

obtuse triangle
A triangle with one obtuse angle.

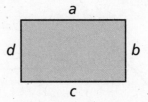

opposite sides
Sides that are across from each other; they do not meet at a point.
Example:
Sides *a* and *c* are opposite.

a

d | | *b*

c

order

Arrange numbers from the least number to the greatest number or from the greatest number to the least number.

Examples:

Least to greatest: 453, 526, 571, 802

Greatest to least: 3,742; 3,608; 3,295

Order of Operations

A set of rules that state the order in which operations should be done.

STEP 1: Compute inside parentheses first.

STEP 2: Multiply and divide from left to right.

STEP 3: Add and subtract from left to right.

ounce (oz)

A U.S. customary unit of weight.

16 ounces = 1 pound

A U.S. customary unit of liquid volume (also called a fluid ounce).

8 ounces = 1 cup

overestimate

Make an estimate that is too big.

P

parallel lines

Lines in the same plane that never intersect are parallel. Line segments and rays that are part of parallel lines are also parallel.

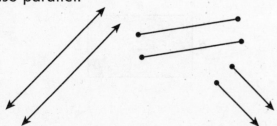

parallelogram

A quadrilateral with both pairs of opposite sides parallel.

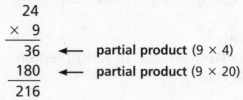

partial product

The product of the ones, or tens, or hundreds, and so on in multidigit multiplication.

Example:

$$\begin{array}{r} 24 \\ \times\ 9 \\ \hline 36 \\ 180 \\ \hline 216 \end{array}$$

$\longleftarrow$ **partial product** (9 × 4)

$\longleftarrow$ **partial product** (9 × 20)

pattern

A sequence that can be described by a rule.

perimeter

The distance around a figure.

perpendicular lines

Lines, line segments, or rays are perpendicular if they form right angles.

Example:

These two lines are perpendicular.

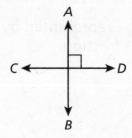

pictograph

A graph that uses pictures or symbols to represent data.

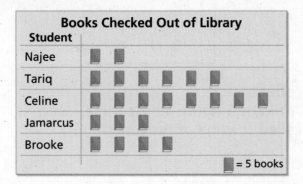

Books Checked Out of Library

Student	
Najee	📕 📕
Tariq	📕 📕 📕 📕 📕
Celine	📕 📕 📕 📕 📕 📕 📕
Jamarcus	📕 📕 📕
Brooke	📕 📕 📕 📕

📕 = 5 books

pint (pt)

A U.S. customary unit of liquid volume that equals 16 fluid ounces.

place value

The value assigned to the place that a digit occupies in a number.

Example:

235
↑

The 2 is in the hundreds place, so its value is 200.

place-value drawing*

A drawing that represents a number. Thousands are represented by vertical rectangles, hundreds are represented by squares, tens are represented by vertical lines, and ones by small circles.

Example:

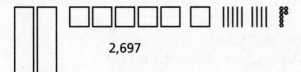

2,697

Place-Value Sections Method*

A method using rectangle drawings to solve multiplication or division problems.

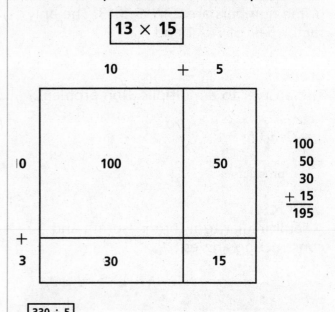

13 × 15

```
            10        +    5

        ┌─────────────┬──────────┐
        │             │          │     100
      10│    100      │    50    │      50
        │             │          │      30
        ├─────────────┼──────────┤    + 15
      + │             │          │     ───
      3 │     30      │    15    │     195
        └─────────────┴──────────┘
```

330 ÷ 5

a.
```
5 │ 330 │
  └─────┘
```

b.
```
        60
5 │ 330 │
  │-300 │
  └─────┘
    30
```

c.
```
        60 +
5 │ 330 │   │
  │-300 │   │
  └─────┘
    30
```

d.
```
        60 +
5 │ 330 │ 30 │
  │-300 │    │
  └──────────┘
    30
```

e.
```
        60 +   6
5 │ 330 │ 30 │
  │-300 │-30 │
  └──────────┘
    30
```

f.
```
        60 +   6 = 66
5 │ 330 │ 30 │
  │-300 │-30 │
  └──────────┘
    30     0
```

point

A location in a plane. It is usually shown by a dot.

polygon

A closed plane figure with sides made of straight line segments.

pound (lb)

A unit of weight in the U.S. customary system.

prefix

A letter or group of letters placed before a word to make a new word.

*A classroom research-based term developed for *Math Expressions*

Glossary

prime number
A number greater than 1 that has 1 and itself as the only factor pair. Examples of prime numbers are 2, 7, and 13. The only factor pair of 7 is 1 and 7.

product
The answer to a multiplication problem.

Example:
9 × 7 = 63

product

protractor
A semicircular tool for measuring and constructing angles.

Q

quadrilateral
A polygon with four sides.

quart (qt)
A U.S. customary unit of liquid volume that equals 32 fluid ounces or 4 cups.

quotient
The answer to a division problem.

Example:

$$\frac{7}{9)\overline{63}}$$

7 is the quotient.

R

ray
Part of a line that has one endpoint and extends without end in one direction.

rectangle
A parallelogram with four right angles.

reflection
A flip of a figure across a line, which is called the line of reflection.

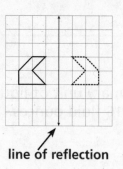

line of reflection

reflex angle
An angle with a measure that is greater than 180° and less than 360°.

remainder
The number left over after dividing two numbers that are not evenly divisible.

Example:

The remainder is 3.

rhombus
A parallelogram with sides of equal length.

right angle
An angle that measures 90°.

right triangle

A triangle with one right angle.

rotation

A turn of a figure in degrees (°), either clockwise or counterclockwise. **Example:**

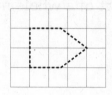

rounding

Finding the nearest ten, hundred, thousand, or some other place value. The usual rounding rule is to round up if the next digit to the right is 5 or more and round down if the next digit to the right is less than 5.

Examples:

463 rounded to the nearest ten is 460.
463 rounded to the nearest hundred is 500.

row

A part of a table or array that contains items arranged horizontally.

S

scalene triangle

A triangle with no equal sides.

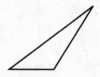

Shortcut Method*

A strategy for multiplying. It is the current common method in the United States.

Step 1	Step 2
$\overset{7}{28}$	$\overset{7}{28}$
$\times\ 9$	$\times\ 9$
2	252

simplest form

A fraction is in simplest form if there is no whole number (other than 1) that divides evenly into the numerator and denominator.

Example:

$\frac{3}{4}$ This fraction is in simplest form because no number divides evenly into 3 and 4.

simplify an expression

Combining like terms and performing operations until all possible terms have been combined.

simplify a fraction

Dividing the numerator and the denominator of a fraction by the same number to make an equivalent fraction made from fewer but larger unit fractions.

Example:

$\frac{5}{10} = \frac{5 \div 5}{10 \div 5} = \frac{1}{2}$

situation equation*

An equation that shows the structure of the information in a problem.

Example:

$35 + n = 40$

solution equation*

An equation that shows the operation that can be used to solve the problem.

Example:

$n = 40 - 35$

*A classroom research-based term developed for *Math Expressions*

Glossary

square
A rectangle with 4 sides of equal length and 4 right angles. It is also a rhombus.

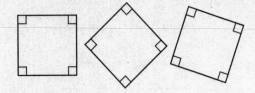

square array
An array in which the number of rows equals the number of columns.

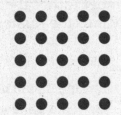

square centimeter (cm²)
A unit of area equal to the area of a square with one-centimeter sides.

square decimeter (dm²)
A unit of area equal to the area of a square with one-decimeter sides.

square foot (ft²)
A unit of area equal to the area of a square with one-foot sides.

square inch (in.²)
A unit of area equal to the area of a square with one-inch sides.

square kilometer (km²)
A unit of area equal to the area of a square with one-kilometer sides.

square meter (m²)
A unit of area equal to the area of a square with one-meter sides.

square mile (mi²)
A unit of area equal to the area of a square with one-mile sides.

square millimeter (mm²)
A unit of area equal to the area of a square with one-millimeter sides.

square number
The product of a whole number and itself.

Example:

$3 \times 3 = 9$

square number

square unit (unit²)
A unit of area equal to the area of a square with one-unit sides.

square yard (yd²)
A unit of area equal to the area of a square with one-yard sides.

standard form
The form of a number written using digits.

Example:
2,145

straight angle
An angle that measures 180°.

sum
The answer when adding two or more addends.

Example:

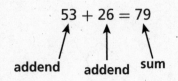

$53 + 26 = 79$

addend   addend   sum

T

table
Data arranged in rows and columns.

tenth
A unit fraction representing one of ten equal parts of a whole, written as 0.1 or $\frac{1}{10}$.

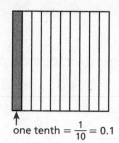

one tenth = $\frac{1}{10}$ = 0.1

12.34
↑
tenth

term
A number, variable, product, or quotient in an expression or equation. Each term is separated by an operation sign (+, −).

Example:
$3n + 5$ has two terms, $3n$ and 5.

thousandth
A unit fraction representing one of one thousand equal parts of a whole, written as 0.001 or $\frac{1}{1,000}$.

ton
A U.S. customary unit of weight that equals 2,000 pounds.

tonne
A metric unit of mass that equals 1,000 kilograms.

total
Sum; the result of addition.

Example:

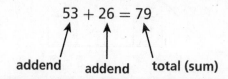

$$53 + 26 = 79$$

addend   addend   total (sum)

transformation
A change in the position of a figure. Rotations, reflections, and translations are types of transformations.

translation
A slide of a figure. Each point of the figure moves the same distance in the same direction.

Example:

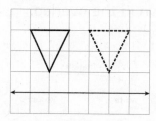

trapezoid
A quadrilateral with exactly one pair of parallel sides.

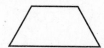

triangle
A polygon with three sides.

U

underestimate
Make an estimate that is too small.

unit
A standard of measurement.

Examples:
Centimeters, pounds, inches, and so on.

Glossary

unit fraction

A fraction whose numerator is 1. It shows one equal part of a whole.

Example:

$\frac{1}{4}$

V

variable

A letter or a symbol that represents a number in an algebraic expression.

Venn diagram

A diagram that uses circles or other shapes to show how sets are related. Items that belong to more than one set are shown in the overlap.

Example:

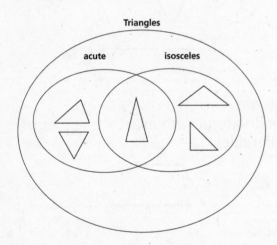

vertex of an angle

A point that is shared by two sides of an angle.

vertex

vertex of a polygon

A point that is shared by two sides of a polygon.

vertex

W

width

The distance across the shorter side of a rectangle.

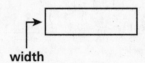

width

word form

The form of a number written using words instead of digits.

Example:
Six hundred thirty-nine

Y

yard (yd)

A U.S. customary unit of length equal to 3 feet.

4.ARO Algebraic Reasoning and Operations

4.ARO.1	Given a multiplication equation, such as $27 = 3 \times 9$, understand how to express it as a comparing situation (example: 27 is 3 *times as many as 9 and 9 times as many as* 3.) Write an equation given a multiplicative-comparison sentence expressed in words.	Unit 4 Lessons 4, 5, 6, 12
4.ARO.2	Solve word problems involving multiplicative comparison by multiplying or dividing; represent the problem by drawing a picture (or diagram) and writing an equation with a symbol for the unknown quantity. Understand the difference between multiplicative and additive comparison.	Unit 4 Lessons 4, 5, 6, 12
4.ARO.3	Use the four operations to solve multi-step word problems involving whole numbers and whole number answers. For division, interpret the remainder. Write an equation, with a letter for the unknown quantity, to represent a problem. Use mental math, compatible numbers, and estimation to determine if an answer is reasonable.	Unit 1 Lessons 8, 11, 12 Unit 2 Lessons 11, 15, 17, 18, 19 Unit 3 Lessons 8, 9, 10, 11, 14 Unit 4 Lessons 7, 8, 9, 12
4.ARO.4	Given a whole number 1–100, find all the pairs of *factors* for the number; understand that a whole number is a *multiple* of its factors. Given a whole number 1–100, find whether it is a multiple of given one-digit number. Decide if a number 1–100 is *prime* or *composite*.	Unit 4 Lessons 10, 12
4.ARO.5	Use numbers or geometric figures to create a pattern that follows a rule (including rules given using variables, e.g., $y = 3x + 5$). Describe other elements of the pattern that are not given in the rule.	Unit 1 Lesson 17 Unit 4 Lessons 10, 11, 12 Unit 8 Lesson 12
4.ARO.6	Create and use input-output rules involving addition, subtraction, multiplication, and division to solve problems in various contexts. Record the inputs and outputs in a chart or table.	Unit 1 Lesson 17 Unit 4 Lesson 11
4.ARO.7	Demonstrate fluency with multiplication and division facts.	Unit 1 Lessons 15, 16, 17, 18

4.PVO Place Value and Operations

4.PVO.1	Understand that the value of a digit in a multi-digit whole number depends on its place in the number; know that each place is 10 times the value of the place to its right.	Unit 1 Lessons 1, 2, 4 Unit 2 Lessons 2, 3
4.PVO.2	Use base-ten numerals, names of numbers, and expanded form to read and write multi-digit numbers. Compare and order multi-digit numbers by using a number line and by demonstrating understanding of the value of digits in each place; record the result using symbols >, <, and =.	Unit 1 Lessons 1, 2, 3, 4, 5 Unit 2 Lessons 4, 10, 12, 16, 19
4.PVO.3	Round multi-digit whole numbers to any place using place value.	Unit 1 Lessons 3, 5, 8, 11, 14 Unit 2 Lessons 5, 17 Unit 3 Lesson 8
4.PVO.4	Use the standard algorithms to add and subtract multi-digit whole numbers, demonstrating fluency.	Unit 1 Lessons 6, 7, 8, 9, 10, 11, 12, 13, 14 Unit 4 Lessons 1, 2, 12
4.PVO.5	Use strategies involving place value and properties of operations to multiply whole numbers containing one- through four-digits by a one-digit number; multiply two two-digit numbers. Use equations, arrays, and/or area models to represent and explain the computation.	Unit 2 Lessons 1, 2, 3, 4, 5, 6, 7, 8, 9, 10, 11, 12, 13, 14, 15, 16, 17, 18, 19 Unit 3 Lesson 14 Unit 4 Lessons 1, 3, 12
4.PVO.6	Use strategies involving place value, properties of operations, and/or the relationship between multiplication and division, to divide whole number dividends with up to four digits by one-digit divisors or up to three digit dividends by two-digit divisors and express the quotients and remainders as whole numbers. Use equations, arrays, and/or area models to represent and explain the computation.	Unit 3 Lessons 1, 2, 3, 4, 5, 6, 7, 8, 9, 10, 11, 12, 13, 14 Unit 4 Lessons 1, 3, 12

© Houghton Mifflin Harcourt Publishing Company

4.FO Fractions and Operations

4.FO.1	Use fraction models to explain why a given fraction $\frac{a}{b}$ is equivalent to a fraction $n \times \frac{a}{n} \times b$; recognize that although the two fractions are the same size, the number and size of their parts are different. Apply this concept for recognizing and creating equivalent fractions.	Unit 7 Lessons 4, 5, 6, 13
4.FO.2	Compare and order fractions (including mixed numbers and fractions greater than 1) that have different denominators or numerators; use methods for comparing such as finding a common denominator or common numerator, or comparing to a benchmark fraction, e.g., $\frac{1}{4}$. Understand that to compare fractions, the size of the wholes must be the same. Use the symbols >, <, or = to record results and justify the result with a model.	Unit 6 Lessons 2, 4, 5, 10 Unit 7 Lessons 1, 2, 3, 6, 13
4.FO.3	Recognize that a fraction $\frac{a}{b}$ with a numerator greater than 1, is the sum of unit fractions.	Unit 6 Lessons 1, 2, 4, 6
4.FO.3.a	Recognize when adding and subtracting fractions, the parts of the same whole are either joined or separated.	Unit 6 Lessons 2, 3, 4, 5, 6, 10
4.FO.3.b	Show different ways to decompose a fraction into the sum of fractions with the same denominators; record each result with an equation. Use a model to justify the decomposition.	Unit 6 Lessons 2, 4, 6, 9
4.FO.3.c	Know how to add and subtract mixed numbers with like denominators. Use methods such as writing each mixed number as an equivalent fraction using properties of operations and the relationship between addition and subtraction.	Unit 6 Lessons 5, 6, 9, 10
4.FO.3.d	Add and subtract fractions with like denominators to solve word problems; understand that like-denominators refer to the same whole. Represent the problem using fraction models and equations.	Unit 6 Lessons 3, 4, 6, 10
4.FO.4	Multiply a fraction and a whole number by applying and extending prior knowledge of multiplication.	Unit 6 Lessons 7, 8
4.FO.4.a	Recognize that fraction $\frac{a}{b}$ is a multiple of a unit fraction, $\frac{1}{b}$.	Unit 6 Lessons 1, 7, 8
4.FO.4.b	Given a fraction $\frac{a}{b}$, recognize that a multiple of the fraction is also a multiple of $\frac{1}{b}$, apply this understanding to multiply a fraction and a whole number.	Unit 6 Lessons 7, 8, 9
4.FO.4.c	Multiply a fraction and a whole number to solve word problems; represent the problems using models and equations.	Unit 6 Lessons 7, 8, 10

Mathematical Standards

4.FO.5	Given a fraction with a denominator of 10, find an equivalent fraction with a denominator of 100; use this method to add a fraction with a denominator of 10 and a fraction with a denominator of 100.	Unit 7 Lesson 6
4.FO.6	Write a fraction with a denominator of 10, 100, or 1000 as a decimal.	Unit 7 Lessons 8, 9, 10, 11, 13, 14
4.FO.7	Compare and order decimals by reasoning about their size and by using place value. Understand that to compare decimals the numbers must refer to the same whole. Use the symbols >, <, or = to record the result and justify the comparison with a model.	Unit 7 Lessons 10, 12, 13, 15
4.FO.8	Round decimals to the nearest tenth.	Unit 7 Lesson 16

4.MDA Measurement and Data Analysis

4.MDA.1	Understand the relative size of units of measure within a given system including, metric (cm, m, km; g, kg; mL, L), customary (oz, lb) and time (s, min, h). Within a given measurement system, rewrite measurements expressed in larger units as smaller units. Use a two-column chart to record equivalent measurements.	Unit 5 Lessons 1, 2, 3, 4, 5, 7, 8
4.MDA.2	Solve word problems involving money, time, distance, liquid volume, and mass using the four operations. Solve problems that contain simple fractions or decimals, and that require rewriting a measurement expressed in a larger unit as a smaller unit. Draw a diagram such as a number line to represent measurements; label the scale of the number line in the given units.	Unit 1 Lessons 6, 13, 14
Unit 2 Lessons 4, 6, 10, 11, 18, 19
Unit 3 Lessons 8, 14
Unit 4 Lessons 7, 8, 12
Unit 5 Lessons 1, 2, 3, 4, 5, 7, 8
Unit 6 Lessons 3, 6, 7, 8, 9, 10
Unit 7 Lessons 10, 11
4.MDA.3	Use the formulas for perimeter and area of rectangles to solve real world or other mathematical problems. Find areas of real-world objects that can be divided into rectangular figures.	Unit 5 Lessons 6, 7, 8
4.MDA.4	Display data involving measurements given in fractions of a unit (example: $\frac{1}{8}$, $\frac{1}{4}$, $\frac{1}{2}$) on a line plot. Use the data from the line plot to solve problems involving addition and subtraction of fractions.	Unit 5 Lesson 3
Unit 6 Lesson 6
Unit 7 Lessons 7, 13
4.MDA.4.a	Use tables, bar graphs, timelines, and Venn diagrams to display data sets.	Unit 1 Lessons 3, 14
Unit 4 Lesson 11
Unit 5 Lessons 2, 3, 4 ,5
Unit 8 Lessons 4, 8
4.MDA.5	Recognize that angles are geometric figures formed by two rays with the same endpoint. Understand angle measurement concepts.	Unit 8 Lessons 1, 2, 3

4.MDA.5.a	Understand that angle measurement is based on the rotation of rays with the same endpoint at the center of a circle and the fraction of the arc formed by the two rays intersecting the circle. Recognize that a one-degree angle (an angle rotation of $\frac{1}{360}$ of a circle) can be used to measure angles.	Unit 8 Lessons 2, 3
4.MDA.5.b	Recognize that an angle that rotates through *n one-degree angles* has an angle measurement of *n degrees*.	Unit 8 Lessons 2, 3
4.MDA.6	Use a protractor to measure angles in whole-number degrees. Draw angles of given measures.	Unit 8 Lessons 2, 3, 5
4.MDA.7	Understand that an angle can be separated into parts that do not overlap and the *sum of the angle measures of the parts* is the angle measure of the whole. Recognize that angle measure is additive. Solve problems involving addition and subtraction to find the measure of an unknown angle presented in a diagram of real-world situations and other mathematical contexts; use an equation with a symbol for the unknown angle to represent the problem.	Unit 8 Lessons 3, 5, 6

4.GSR Geometry and Spatial Reasoning

4.GSR.1	Identify and draw points, lines, line segments, rays, angles (right, acute, obtuse), parallel lines, perpendicular lines, and intersecting lines, and recognize them in two-dimensional figures.	Unit 8 Lessons 1, 2, 3, 4, 5, 7, 8, 9, 10, 12
4.GSR.2	Classify two-dimensional figures by determining whether or not they have parallel or perpendicular lines, or angles of a given size. Describe, classify and draw quadrilaterals, including squares, rectangles, trapezoids, rhombuses, parallelograms and kites. Identify right triangles and understand that they comprise a specific category of triangles.	Unit 8 Lessons 4, 8, 9, 10, 12
4.GSR.3	Recognize that when a two-dimensional figure can be folded along a line into matching parts, the fold-line is called a *line of symmetry*. Identify figures with line symmetry.	Unit 8 Lessons 11, 12
4.GSR.4	Apply translations (slides) to figures.	Unit 8 Lessons 13, 14
4.GSR.5	Apply reflections (flips) to figures by reflecting over vertical or horizontal lines and relate reflections to lines of symmetry.	Unit 8 Lessons 13, 14
4.GSR.6	Apply rotations (turns) of 90° clockwise or counterclockwise.	Unit 8 Lessons 13, 14
4.GSR.7	Recognize that translations, reflections and rotations preserve congruency and use them to show that two figures are congruent.	Unit 8 Lessons 13, 14

Mathematical Processes and Practices

MPP1
Problem Solving

Unit 1 Lessons 2, 3, 5, 6, 7, 8, 12, 13, 14, 17, 18
Unit 2 Lessons 2, 3, 4, 5, 6, 7, 10, 11, 13, 14, 15, 16, 17, 18, 19
Unit 3 Lessons 2, 5, 6, 7, 8, 9, 10, 11, 12, 14
Unit 4 Lessons 2, 3, 4, 5, 6, 7, 8, 9, 11, 12
Unit 5 Lessons 1, 2, 3, 5, 6, 7, 8
Unit 6 Lessons 5, 6, 7, 10
Unit 7 Lessons 1, 2, 3, 4, 6, 7, 8, 9, 10, 11, 13, 15
Unit 8 Lessons 5, 6, 7, 8, 12, 13, 14

MPP2
Abstract and Quantitative Reasoning

Unit 1 Lessons 1, 3, 4, 5, 6, 8, 9, 14, 15, 16, 17, 18
Unit 2 Lessons 2, 4, 5, 6, 7, 8, 9, 10, 11, 13, 15, 16, 17, 19
Unit 3 Lessons 1, 3, 5, 7, 8, 11, 13
Unit 4 Lessons 1, 2, 3, 4, 5, 6, 11, 12
Unit 5 Lessons 2, 6, 7, 8
Unit 6 Lessons 1, 2, 3, 4, 7, 10
Unit 7 Lessons 1, 2, 9, 10, 13
Unit 8 Lessons 3, 5, 6, 12, 13, 14

MPP3
Use and Evaluate Logical Reasoning

Unit 1 Lessons 1, 2, 3, 4, 5, 6, 7, 8, 9, 10, 11, 12, 13, 14, 15, 16, 18
Unit 2 Lessons 1, 2, 3, 4, 5, 6, 7, 8, 9, 10, 11, 12, 13, 14, 15, 16, 17, 18, 19
Unit 3 Lessons 1, 2, 3, 4, 5, 6, 7, 8, 9, 10, 11, 12, 13, 14
Unit 4 Lessons 1, 2, 3, 4, 5, 6, 7, 8, 9, 10, 11, 12
Unit 5 Lessons 1, 2, 3, 4, 5, 6, 7, 8
Unit 6 Lessons 1, 2, 3, 4, 5, 6, 7, 8, 9, 10
Unit 7 Lessons 1, 2, 3, 4, 5, 6, 7, 8, 9, 10, 11, 12, 13, 14, 15
Unit 8 Lessons 1, 2, 3, 4, 5, 6, 7, 8, 9, 10, 11, 12, 13, 14

MPP4
Mathematical Modeling

Unit 1 Lessons 1, 2, 3, 4, 6, 9, 10, 12, 13, 14
Unit 2 Lessons 1, 2, 4, 5, 6, 7, 8, 10, 12, 16, 19
Unit 3 Lessons 1, 2, 3, 4, 10, 11
Unit 4 Lessons 2, 3, 4, 5, 8, 9, 10, 11, 12
Unit 5 Lessons 4, 6, 7, 8
Unit 6 Lessons 1, 3, 4, 5, 6, 7, 8, 10
Unit 7 Lessons 2, 3, 5, 7, 8, 9, 10, 11, 12, 13, 14, 15, 16
Unit 8 Lessons 2, 5, 6, 12, 13, 14

MPP5

Use Mathematical Tools

Unit 1 Lessons 1, 2, 3, 4, 6, 9, 14, 15, 16, 17, 18
Unit 2 Lessons 1, 4, 5, 6, 8, 10, 11, 12, 16, 19
Unit 3 Lessons 3, 4, 10, 11
Unit 4 Lessons 2, 10, 11, 12
Unit 5 Lessons 1, 4, 5, 6, 7, 8
Unit 6 Lessons 1, 2, 3, 4, 8, 9, 10
Unit 7 Lessons 1, 2, 4, 5, 9, 10, 11, 12, 13, 14, 15
Unit 8 Lessons 1, 2, 4, 5, 7, 8, 9, 10, 11, 12, 13

MPP6

Use Precise Mathematical Language

Unit 1 Lessons 1, 2, 3, 4, 5, 6, 7, 8, 9, 10, 11, 12, 13, 14, 15, 16, 18
Unit 2 Lessons 1, 2, 3, 4, 5, 6, 7, 8, 9, 10, 11, 12, 13, 14, 15, 16, 17, 18, 19
Unit 3 Lessons 1, 2, 3, 4, 5, 6, 7, 8, 9, 10, 11, 12, 13, 14
Unit 4 Lessons 1, 2, 3, 4, 5, 6, 7, 8, 9, 10, 11, 12, 13, 14
Unit 5 Lessons 1, 2, 3, 4, 5, 6, 7, 8
Unit 6 Lessons 1, 2, 3, 4, 5, 6, 7, 8, 9, 10
Unit 7 Lessons 1, 2, 3, 4, 5, 6, 7, 8, 9, 10, 11, 12, 13, 14, 15, 16
Unit 8 Lessons 1, 2, 3, 4, 5, 6, 7, 8, 9, 10, 11, 12, 13, 14

MPP7

See Structure

Unit 1 Lessons 1, 2, 4, 9, 13, 14, 16, 17
Unit 2 Lessons 2, 3, 6, 8, 9, 10, 13, 16, 17, 19
Unit 3 Lessons 1, 3, 10, 11
Unit 4 Lessons 1, 2, 3, 5, 10, 11, 12
Unit 5 Lessons 1, 2, 4, 8
Unit 6 Lessons 1, 4, 5, 10
Unit 7 Lessons 2, 6, 9, 10, 11, 12, 13
Unit 8 Lessons 1, 2, 4, 7, 8, 9, 10, 14

MPP8

Generalize

Unit 1 Lessons 3, 4, 5, 6, 7, 10, 11, 14, 16
Unit 2 Lessons 1, 2, 3, 5, 7, 8, 15, 17, 19
Unit 3 Lessons 1, 3, 5, 6, 11, 13
Unit 4 Lessons 1, 2, 10, 11, 12
Unit 5 Lessons 1, 4, 6, 8
Unit 6 Lessons 2, 7, 9, 10
Unit 7 Lessons 1, 3, 6, 8, 10, 11, 13, 14
Unit 8 Lessons 1, 3, 4, 9, 10, 11, 12

Index

B

C

D

© Houghton Mifflin Harcourt Publishing Company

Index

H

I

K

L

O

Obtuse angle, 397–398, 403–404, 407–408, 439

Obtuse triangle, 431–432, 434

Order of Operations, 416

Ounces, 257, 260

Overestimate, 173

P

Parallel lines, 423, 425, 445

Parallelogram, 428, 430, 431–432, 433, 434

Partial products, 89

Patterns, 223, 230
extending, 224
in fraction bars, 288
growing, 224
in money, 362
writing a rule, 227

Penny, 361, 366

Perimeter, 261, 265
calculating, 265–266
of complex figures, 267–269, 270

Perpendicular lines, 424–425, 445

Perpendicular sides, 440

Pictographs, 205

Pint (pt), 259

Place Value
chart, 7, 367, 377
comparing, 10, 13
dot array, 3, 105
hundreds and thousands, 3
drawings, 4–6
hundreds, 3–6, 76
ones, 3–6
tens, 3–6
groups, 75–76
identify, 7, 11
to millions, 13–14,

model hundreds and thousands, 3–8, 11–12, 95–98, 115–116
rounding, 9, 16
Secret Code Cards
Decimal, 366A–366B, 370A–370B, 378A–378B
Whole Number, 6A–6D
tenths and hundredths, 365–366
thousandths, 377, 379
to thousands, 3–8
ungrouping with zeros, 29
write, 8, 11–12
zeros in, 29

Place Value Drawings
models, 3, 4, 6, 75, 87, 88

Point, 395–396

Polygons, 435. *See also* **Geometry.**
classify, 439–440
decompose, 431–436
Polygon Cards, 440A
triangles, 407–412

Pounds, 257–258

Prime number, 220

Problem solving. *See also* **Word problems.**
addition, 19–21
comparison problems, 199, 201, 203
different problem types, 37
division, 152
by factoring, 74
with line plots, 355–356
multi-step, 35
and sharing solutions, 36, 37–38
steps of the problem, 209, 211–212
using equations, 193–194, 196, 211–212
using estimation, 23–24

Problem Types, S8–S12

Product Cards, 46A–46J

Products, 45. *See also* **Multiplication.**
checking, 176
estimating of, 85, 109, 110, 120
of ones, 73
partial, 89
of tens, 76

Index

© Houghton Mifflin Harcourt Publishing Company

Index

Illustrator: Josh Brill

Did you ever try to use shapes to draw animals like the lemur on the cover?

Over the last 10 years Josh has been using geometric shapes to design his animals. His aim is to keep the animal drawings simple and use color to make them appealing.

Add some color to the lemur Josh drew. Then try drawing a cat or dog or some other animal using the shapes below.

Shape Toolbox